ISHI
&
ELVIS

ISHI
&
ELVIS

JIM HAMM

BOIS
d'ARC
PRESS

ISBN 0-9645741-0-1

ACKNOWLEDGMENTS

Years ago The Master, John Graves, offered encouragement when it was most needed, enticing me against all inclination to remain in front of the keyboard. Tim Baker and Jim Mitchell offered ideas and critique of this manuscript, for which I remain in their debt. Steve Allely, gifted artist with both brush and bow-stave, provided the illustrations used throughout. Fly fishermen might find the short piece on heavenly hunting herein vaguely familiar, for a similar parable was told about them by G. E. M. Skues in 1947.

And special thanks to those with whom I've shared a campfire over the years, who remain part of the lifeblood of that greater heartbeat out beyond the circle of lights.

To Donna, for cheerfully tolerating a writer.

ONE

T HE first eager cool front of autumn had finally shoved back summer's smothering heat and triggered rain the night before, making tracking just possible if you looked closely enough for hints of a deer's passage between the rocks. Since Frank Sherwood and I had been finding scattered deer sign all morning, a single heart-shaped footprint pressed into the mud did not, at first, seem particularly important. We knelt beside the fence where deer habitually jumping over had beaten down the vegetation on both sides to bare dirt.

After pressing a callused thumb into the rain-sculpted soil, Frank studied the imprint, then focused on the track and offered, "Big deer. And a pretty fair trail through here."

"Buck or doe?" I asked blandly, knowing I would be forced to accept whatever he said since I couldn't tell the difference.

"Hard to say from just one track," he answered, shaking his head, "but I'd guess a buck."

Since he was an instructor at a tracking school, I took his word for it. Glancing to the west, I tried to decide what to do about the information, while noting with some satisfaction that the vegetation on our side of the fence was beginning to recover from "being goated," in the idiom of the Texas Hill Country. Years of foraging by hundreds of Angora goats, while no doubt making money for the previous landowner, had stripped away the protective covering of grass, leaving exposed the limestone bones of the earth. You can run a lot of goats for a lot of years without killing the desirable redbuds, sumacs, and hackberries, but when I acquired the ranch a few months earlier none of these plants could be found, though they thrived along roadways nearby. The clumps of cedar and persimmon, normally prolific and hard to control, had mostly been pruned as high as a goat could reach and in many cases killed from the intense use.

Upon closing the deal for this rocky seven hundred acres, I immediately banned goats forever and now welcomed the slowly returning brush for deer cover and forage. You are what you dream, I suppose, so that made me a ranch owner — though a shrewder buyer might have bought a different property, one with no trace of goat usage, one on which the deer flourished in greater numbers. But the crystalline creek winding across the bottom land on one end of the ranch was diving gracefully over its rock ledges the first time I saw it, and besides, the Federal Land Bank allowed me to sink into hock up to my earlobes to buy the place. Like I said, a shrewder buyer might have bought a different property...

Shafts of sunlight slanting through the leaves of scattered live oaks and crimson Spanish oaks abruptly ended their journey through space by splashing the ground around us. The single knife-edged track stared back without blinking, unmoved by any predatory urges on our part.

"He left your place just before daylight," Frank remarked, glancing up through the fence and pointing with his lips. "He's over there somewhere, bedded down in the thick stuff."

It was becoming clear that most deer spent the daylight hours in the cedar and oak thickets on an adjacent ranch just over the fence to the south. At night they meandered back over to eat the tender shoots the brush was regenerating after banishment of the voracious goats. October bow season had found me with no clear idea of where to hunt, but this fence crossing was the best spot we had found during the morning's scout, offering hope that the buck might return tonight by the same route while there was still light enough to see.

Where to set up? For a shot with a longbow it had to be close, twenty yards or less. Sniping an unsuspecting deer at long range with a scoped rifle is relatively easy, but working to within "wolf range," where deer have been specifically bred for hundreds of thousands of years to avoid danger, becomes a study in frustration. Not only must you remain undetected by his hyper-sensitive nose, ears, and eyes until he finally makes his way close enough, you must draw the bow, causing motion and sound no matter how you strive to minimize it. So to have any prospect for success the stand location is all-important.

I pointed to a living room-sized island of cedar and stunted liveoaks twenty yards away, "Let's cut an opening in the middle of those trees to stand and a shooting lane on this side where the trail goes by."

Frank nodded, "We need to make the opening big, cause I'm a big guy."

"Who says this is your spot?"

"I'm a guest," Frank smiled, "and guests always get first choice."

I reminded him he was lucky to even be allowed to visit Texas, much less hunt here, since he's from New Jersey. He quickly denied it, pointing out that he was born and raised in Washington State.

"That makes it even worse," I insisted, "since you *moved* to New Jersey."

As we worked into the middle of the tangle, he muttered something about the deer in New Jersey at least having visible antlers. In four days of hunting here, we had seen a single male deer, a five month old buck with half-inch spikes. After using our knives to cut out a place big enough to stand and draw a bow, I cleared a narrow shooting lane out toward the trail. A perfect set-up, wind from the south at the deer's back, plenty of cover to draw the bow without being seen, then an opening to shoot through as the animal passed by fifteen yards away. A dunk shot. Now all we needed was a deer.

"Even a New Jerzoid should be able to kill a buck here," I announced as we finished.

Frank holstered his tongue and made no reply, for once, but glanced at the sun, strung his longbow, and worked his way into the stand.

"I guess I'll stay," his voice floated out of the brush, "nothing much else to do."

I suspected then he might have noticed something about the track he wasn't mentioning.

Late that evening, I poked the fire and let its radiance brush the cool air away from my face. Camp consisted of an old trailer set among a clump of liveoaks on one of the highest points on the ranch, allowing me to soak in the unimpeded ten-mile view to the west. A great lavender and cobalt swirl of clouds were all that remained of a sunset more suited to psychedelic imagination than reality. Velvet blackness crept closer as the light slowly faded. A horned owl's booming hoot, sounding eager to begin the night, echoed from one of the giant pecan trees down along the creek. I was finally beginning to feel less of a stranger here as intricacies of dirt and water and trees and animals and weather began slowly revealing themselves. Much yet to learn, however, and a lifetime, or half of one, anyway, seemed scarcely enough time.

Earlier in the afternoon, I had seen only a couple of does along the fringe of woods beside a field. The oats appeared to have been mowed from heavy grazing, though the deer rarely showed themselves in the open during daylight. A flock of turkeys, ten or fifteen by the sound of them, had flown to roost in some sycamores along the creek with a great deal of flapping and yelping...

Frank shuffled into the firelight, his unstrung bow in one hand, the orange feathers of his arrows in a back quiver peeking over his right shoulder. He looked as though he'd eaten a sour plum.

Moving up to the fire, he cleared his throat. "Well, you have at least one nice buck living here."

That was comforting, since in the past two months I had only seen does, spikes, and forkhorn bucks, and not many of those.

"Real wide eight-point, with long tines and heavy beams," he added.

"Where is he?"

"He was ten yards away. I got a perfect look at him."

"Ten yards? Why didn't you shoot him?"

Frank directed a withering look my way. "'Cause you cut the shooting lane facing the wrong direction."

"What?" I protested, "you had an easy shot to the trail."

"He got big by not being stupid," he said, finally breaking into a grin, "he wasn't on the trail."

Frank explained that at dusk he watched a doe and yearling jump the fence at the crossing and walk past on the trail, exactly as expected. As the two deer disappeared among the scattered trees, he had heard a tiny noise and glanced over his shoulder to see the buck strolling past just behind him.

Frank held hands out beside his head, fingers spread, to indicate something about the size of a reindeer. "He was really close, but there was no way to get an arrow through all that brush."

Like the man said, the buck wasn't stupid — as I was soon to discover for myself — and was traveling parallel to the trail.

"Bad as I hate to admit it," Frank reflected, "it was worth the trip just to get that close to such a buck."

It seems every place has its legends about a particular big deer — *Muy Grande*, they call him in South Texas — which the hunters dream about but never quite outmaneuver. The embryonic legend about the deer Frank had seen somehow made this ranch seem whole. It was only now becoming clear to me how detrimental the overstocked goats had been to the deer and how many years it would take the land to recover — still another comment, perhaps, on the shrewdness of the buyer. With the discovery of this big buck, envisioned projects which would benefit wildlife only over the course of years or even decades suddenly became something more than the puttering of a new owner. The presence of a *Muy Grande* here gave focus to the entire ranch.

I had taken some nice bucks over the years, a couple of which were really nice, though it was always simply luck because I seldom knew that specific deer was in the area. I had never focused on just one particular buck. Though yet to see him, I made up my mind to hunt this deer I would eventually come to know as Elvis (because, like The King these days, he created such a stir on the rare occasions he chose to put in an appearance). I would concentrate on Elvis and no other deer.

And use a bow to plant feathered death within him.

TWO

NORMALLY, Thanksgiving came too early for any real winter weather here in Central Texas, but a "blue norther" as they're known in this part of the country had been blowing. I've never been sure if the name refers to the color of the clouds or the color of your lips if you spend too much time outside in one, but we'd seen two and a half days of sleet, fifteen degree temperatures, and thirty mile an hour winds, enough to pin down both deer and deer hunters. When the storm finally released its grip this morning and the sun broke through the clouds the icy coating on the trees looked like polished armor dazzling in the sunlight.

Earlier in the afternoon, my oldest son and I had climbed into chain-on tree stands at one end of the oat field. Our liveoaks stood thirty yards apart with deer trails winding past. Hunting from a tree simplified the difficulty of drawing a bow on a deer at close range since they generally don't look up, though deer heavily hunted from treestands quickly adapt by gazing up like dedicated bird watchers. Climbing trees was no doubt a prehistoric bowhunting trick, and was even written about by Herodotus in 450 B.C. when he described the hunting by Scythians in Central Asia.

At thirteen, Lee had been hunting with a bow for a couple of years, though he had yet to see a deer up close. We were watching plenty of deer today, however. They were hungry after waiting out the storm huddled under some bush and found the oats irresistible. At least ten does and yearlings fed in the sixteen acre field, though it was still an hour until sunset. Lee was a decent shot with the wooden longbow I had made for him, but the two does which had earlier walked directly under my stand were out of his twenty yard range. We sat silently in our trees, wrapped in a cloak of invisibility, watching the deer and waiting.

Clearly, through some oversight, Elvis had not been informed of The Plan. I had hunted him hard for more than a month since he first passed Frank's brush blind, and hadn't been rewarded with so much as a glimpse of him, much less a shot. At the suggestion of a friend who knew about my mission, Paul Crow, I had gone so far as to stop by the Post Office and purchase an Elvis stamp to place on the back of my hunting license, right beside the space reserved for the Federal Migratory Bird Hunting and Conservation Stamp. But even that didn't help.

Most weekends, as well as any other time which was free (and some which wasn't) had found me here at the ranch searching for the elusive deer. I had hunted throughout the rut, one of the rare times you'll see a mature buck in good light and about the only time he's vulnerable, when the madness of breeding possesses him and he loses some of his habitual caution. The rut becomes a time of frantic activity, with bucks chasing does in heat throughout the day, or fighting each other, or wandering about looking for does. But Elvis failed to make his scheduled appearance. With the rut winding down now, my hopes for a chance at him were fading, and I began wondering if Frank might have invented the whole episode...

A small buck trotted from the thick fringe of trees into the far end of the oat field, creating a minor ripple among the does and yearlings as they moved aside to allow the more dominant animal to pass. Far from the benign, gentle creatures we sometimes envision, deer can be aggressive, with a distinct pecking order.

Though the deer hierarchy appears peaceful at a casual glance, it is constantly challenged from below in subtle ways, such as crowding a higher ranking animal in a feeding area. Sometimes things are not so subtle, as when flattened ears or the glare from a dominant animal fails to intimidate a lesser deer. At such times I've watched does slash at each other with their front feet or even bite each other on the ear. And of course once in a great while two bucks who think they are evenly matched get into blood-slinging fights during the rut, with one or both sometimes dying from the combat.

I hoped Lee would at least get a close look at a deer today whether or not he got a shot, to experience one of humanity's oldest adrenaline floods before discovering an even older male human passion, girls, in a year or two. Then, he would probably fling his bow into the corner to gather dust for ten or fifteen years. But once the madness of the rut finally left him, he might just remember the ancient impulse of the hunter and pick it up again. I couldn't see him through the thick foliage of the liveoaks, but knew he was watching the deer. The small buck casually checked out a couple of does on the off chance one might still be in heat. He soon grazed with the rest, though grazing is a misnomer, really, since deer are far pickier than cattle and eat few of the same plants. Only a fraction of a deer's diet consists of grass, as they prefer weeds rich in protein and minerals, acorns, the tender new growth of brush, and crops like wheat and oats since they are among the few plants green and palatable this time of year.

Thin streaks of frozen clouds painted across the heavens served as the storm's farewell. Does by ones and twos had continued entering the oats as the sun dropped behind the line of trees along the western border of the field. Sixteen now fed, scattered in small groups. The deer we'd been watching this afternoon were by far the most I'd seen at one time during daylight, though spotlight counts at night showed about twenty-five or thirty using the entire place, a disappointing number for this part of the county.

While gazing at the sunset, I reflected on the quest for Elvis. The object of hunting him with a bow was not, as might be supposed, simply a dead deer, since deer were far easier killed with a rifle. Since I wasn't hungry, and the deer population fell well within the bounds of the habitat, I had earlier passed on the two doe which walked under my tree. The point of hunting only Elvis, it seemed, lay in the challenge rather than merely a dead deer, as taking him with a bow registered almost off of the difficulty scale. A buck old enough to attain such size had seen scores of hunting tactics, every one of which he had found instructive. A mature whitetail buck, living in the shadow of humans, may be the most difficult animal on the planet to hunt with a bow at close range. I had pursued deer since the age of ten, more than thirty years, but only now felt myself a competent enough predator to try for such a deer with a bow. Bowhunting allows you to become a direct participant in the intricate dance of life, and yes, death, too. Better to take such a role than to pass a lifetime as a neutral observer with no interest in the outcome, like a bored alien staring through the porthole of his spaceship. Therein, I finally decided, lay the compulsion — participation. Gardeners and beekeepers and fly fishermen will understand...

I noticed another ripple among the deer at the far end of the oats, this one more pronounced than the first. The small buck had now vanished. A deer far bigger than the others trotted from one doe to another, and even at over three hundred yards his antlers were plainly visible. I fumbled for the small set of binoculars in my pocket, quickly adjusted them, and gasped softly at the biggest deer I had ever seen. Who else? It had to be Elvis, right here in the open. The spread of his antlers reached far wider than his ears, close to twenty inches. They flashed like ivory in the late afternoon sun. His legs looked stubby, but only because he was so thick through the chest, the sign of a mature deer at least four and a half years old. The way he checked out the scattered does made it clear he wasn't ready for the rut to be over. He made his way down the field, sniffing briefly at each doe before moving on.

Glancing in Lee's direction, I wondered if he could see the buck, while hoping that his composure was better than mine. I was suddenly breathing like a fat man in a marathon. Elvis finally moved to within a hundred yards of our end of the field and investigated the last does. I slipped a small grunt tube from a pocket and gently blew it. The sound imitates the grunt a buck makes — sounding for all the world like a soft belch — when he's following a doe in heat. Elvis paid no attention. I gave a sharper grunt, wondering if he'd heard me. He whirled, then froze, ears flared wide, staring at the woods behind me. One more soft grunt and here he came, determined to thrash this interloping buck and take his doe. He ran to within fifteen yards of Lee's tree — about forty yards from me — then stopped and glared past us, searching for the fictitious buck.

Lee didn't understand how big this deer was, I hoped, and how rarely he would have a chance like this. I hardly realized I was holding my breath, waiting for his arrow. A perfect opportunity for him, the deer of a lifetime broadside with his attention diverted elsewhere. This would be great, getting to watch Lee take his first shot at a deer, and at Elvis to boot. Though it was still cold, the sweat trickled down the back of my neck. Wasn't he going to shoot? Elvis took a couple of stiff-legged steps, nervous because he couldn't find the deer he thought he'd heard. He glanced over his shoulder at the does in the field, and I grunted softly once again. He whirled and stared up at the tree where I sat. He couldn't see me but he had me nailed. Wasn't Lee ever going to shoot? Couldn't he see the deer? Was he waiting for a really big one?

Elvis turned and glided away from us with that fluid head-lowered trot that big bucks use. In a moment he disappeared into the trees on the far side of the field. I blinked a couple of times, scarcely believing he had put in such an outrageous appearance, sauntering right up to us. A slight shiver shook through me, then grew, the common culmination of such intense concentration and anticipation. My wife claims I'm an adrenaline junkie, and she may be right. I've experienced a dozen such encounters over the years for every shot taken. And it wasn't just big bucks which caused this ancient adrenaline-induced focusing, but also little ones, and does, too, whenever you looked at a particular animal with the squint-eyed gaze of a predator, wanting the shot, whether it came or not.

The drying sweat on my neck sucked away the heat in the frigid air, prompting another shiver. Wanting a close look at Elvis' tracks for future reference, since the light was quickly ebbing I lowered the bow with a cord and climbed down from my perch. The remaining deer in the field scattered for cover, white tails flagging in alarm. Passing Lee's tree, I motioned for him to stay put and he nodded, eyes round as an owl's.

The tracks showed clearly in the damp soil of the field. Big, really big. Considerably bigger than any others I had seen and pressed deeply from his weight. Kneeling, I examined the tracks closely for several minutes before noticing the tips of his hooves left a blunt imprint, unlike the sharper tips from a younger deer. Given their size and blunt tips, his tracks would now be unmistakable. I firmly rededicated myself to the pursuit of Elvis. He hadn't seen the last of me, for there remained a great deal to learn from him.

When I finally helped Lee down from his tree he was still shaking, too. "Did you see him?" he whispered, "did you?"

We began hiking toward camp. "Yeah. Why didn't you shoot?"

"A big branch and a bunch of leaves were in the way. He was right there but the branch was in the way. Did you see how he just stood there?"

"Yep."

"I didn't know deer got that big. Did you see how big he was?"

"I sure did."

"That's the buck you've been telling me about, isn't it?"

I placed a hand on his shoulder and he didn't pull away, as adolescents are wont to do. "He is, indeed."

"Now I know why you've been spending so much time down here."

If a dead deer was the sole object of hunting then we had failed miserably, father and son, but failure was the farthest thing from my mind as we strolled along in the dark. I was contemplating how Lee would remember this day for the rest of his life. And so would I.

THREE

THE skill of bowmaking evolved into artistry for the old-timers. They crafted their bows from a single piece of wood, somehow making do with this most natural of raw materials — for about fifteen thousand years. I would follow their lead and hunt Elvis with a hand-made wooden bow, an act of blasphemy, perhaps, to those who view with favor modern mass-produced weapons. But it seemed sacrilegious, somehow, to have any soul-less machinery between me and a deer like Elvis. Something would be lacking if I shot him from another area code with a scoped rifle, or even from fifty yards with a compound bow, either of which could have already killed him in the oat field. The more technology the more psychic distance between hunter and deer, so I would make a new bow for the sole purpose of hunting Elvis the hard way, on primordial terms, one on one — may the best animal win.

While meandering around an absentee neighbor's bottom land along the creek, exploring and trespassing, as usual, I discovered and later returned to cut the small Osage orange tree which would be transformed into this bow. Though I wasn't seen, ranch owners are generally little concerned at finding a neighbor on their land, but they take a dim, tight-lipped view of such an incursion from an outsider, and particularly from a lost city-bred, rifle-armed deer hunter (though if said hunter is halfway polite the landowner usually gives him a pickup ride back to his camp).

The topic of conversation down at the coffee shop the week before deer season always centers around the imminent invasion by the city hunters. People ignorant of the realities of living from the land are known for leaving gates open, allowing the bull to visit the heifers ahead of schedule; scattering beer cans, candy wrappers, toilet paper, and spent cartridges by the dozens; burning off pastures with tossed cigarettes and untended fires; shooting deer they are later unable to find, as well as occasionally livestock and even each other; swaggering about town in full camo with twelve inch Bowie knives ready at the hip. These and other infractions of common sense and good manners occur every year, to the disgust of ranchers and the detriment of conscientious hunters, who often lease a place for decades and pass the lease down to their children, in the process becoming life-long friends of the landowner.

Most country folk look upon hunter antics with wry resignation, but if a stray hunter should have the bad taste to actually shoot a deer somewhere besides the land he has leased, things can become interesting. In one recent case in our area, a big-city poacher cut a ten foot game-proof fence to trespass and kill a huge trophy whitetail with a rifle. After game wardens investigated, he was identified and arrested, the deer antlers confiscated. He was fined only six hundred dollars for killing the deer, but was also charged with a third degree felony *for cutting the fence* — a transgression which cost him three year's probation, $2,655 in restitution to the landowner, $1000 in fines to the state, two hundred hours of community service, plus court costs. The locals, myself included, applauded...

Anyway, since the statute of limitations has about run out, I may as well admit I rustled the tree growing upstream from my place — there are, after all, higher laws concerning good bow wood. The six-inch diameter trunk was remarkably straight for the notoriously crooked Osage. I cut the tree after placing a pinch of tobacco at its base and silently offering my assurances that its spirit would live on through the weapon I would fashion. Romantic foolishness, most likely, but then those given to making wooden bows are susceptible to such musings, and after starting on the trail of Elvis I was glad for making the effort since there was no sense taking any chances on offending the chosen tree. Romantic foolishness, almost certainly...

The tree was split into quarters just after felling, the ends coated with glue to prevent drying cracks. Now, with deer season winding down in mid-December, the wood had cured for about four months and was ready to begin its rebirth. The bark and cream-colored sapwood were first chopped free with hatchet and drawknife, a tough job since Osage orange is North America's densest native wood. The common name for this thorny tree is bois d'arc (literally French for "wood of the bow") a term corrupted here in typical Texas fashion to "board ark", though this had nothing to do with lumber since the wood was too crooked and knotty to make anything save the occasional fence post.

Once the sapwood was free, I used the drawknife and a pocketknife to scrape the electric-yellow heartwood, a crucial part of making a bois d'arc bow. The back of the bow must be reduced to one annual growth ring to resist the stretching forces when the bow is drawn. The scrapers became time machines, carefully peeling away year after year of the growth rings, a thick one when the summer rains fell heavy and often, a couple of thin ones together reflecting dry years, when the tree struggled to live and could spare little fat for putting on extra wood. Finally, after a few hour's work, the leisurely journey through time was complete, with a growth ring from several years in the past exposed on the back, perhaps the year Elvis or one of my sons was born. The back of the bow dipped here, swept up and over a knot there, revealing the hidden soul of the tree waiting for all of this time — hopefully — for a bowyer to happen along and combine his will with that of the wood.

I'm a dinosaur, I'll admit, but have been making all-wood bows for years, learning from the oldest teacher, trial and error, learning through broken bows and disappointments, learning while my long-suffering wife watched without a word as the pile of wood shavings grew in the center of the living room floor on cold winter evenings. The patient scraping and shaping and sanding, putting your experience and sweat and sometimes a little blood into the wood connects a modern bowmaker to all of the bowyers in the past. The growing blisters on soft hands gives one an appreciation for the first inventive savage squatted on his haunches working his bowstave with a simple flint scraper, his work given impetus by his growling belly and the nearby women and children depending upon his skill to keep them fed another day. And keep them fed he did, for hundreds of generations, using the same technology one uses today in one's living room, if one's wife is understanding. Our primitive hunter patiently fashioned his bow and stone-tipped arrows, with which he provided meat to his delighted family and friends, as well as kept lions and bears from sampling too often the members of his band.

And so it was for fifteen thousand years or so, every generation passing on its bowmaking and hunting skills to the next, across every continent, until the advent of agriculture. Tim Baker, a friend from Berkeley with whom I regularly engage in what he terms "recreational arguing," maintains that the apple in the creation story of Adam and Eve doesn't represent knowledge at all but rather agriculture. Once man had bitten the domesticated crop and been tempted from the hunting and gathering garden, the subjugation of the natural world and the long slide to the crowded present was inevitable. Forgive us this day our daily bread.

In any case, after the advent of agriculture, men invented more exciting uses for their bows — organized warfare. Even a casual reading of history shows that the venerable bow has played a role in virtually every empire, often the pivotal role. Of the mounted Scythians a Biblical contemporary wrote, "Their quivers are like an open grave. They will eat your harvest and bread, they will eat your sons and daughters, they will eat your grapes and figs."

Delightful lads, whooping and riding and raping and dining across most of Asia and a big chunk of Europe. I'll have to ask Frank whether their descendants migrated to New Jersey or Washington State...

Once the back of the bois d'arc stave had been worked to a single growth ring, the outline of the bow was drawn out in pencil. It stood sixty-eight inches tall, straight for the most part but swelling around the knots, about a dozen in all, and the parallel sides followed the snaky grain near one end. The tips were made small and delicate, both for aesthetics and to reduce the mass the bow had to accelerate with each shot, which slightly increased arrow speed. I suppose carefully imposing your will upon the natural flow of the wood could be considered artwork of a kind, though a junior high art teacher once assured me I was artistically declined.

After rasping the outline of the weapon down to the pencil lines, the real bowmaking began — making the erstwhile fence post bend. As I began removing wood from the belly of the bow with the rasp, I reflected upon how the soft hum of a bowstring seems to resonate within our very DNA, transcending race and time and distance. Throughout the world, for fifteen millennium tens of thousands of bows had been made by men to feed and protect their families and eventually, after we fell from grace from the hunting and gathering garden, to perpetrate glorious, bloody deeds. Throughout all of history probably the blood-thirstiest Homo Sapiens to ever draw breath were not some primitive people but our English forbears, who perpetrated mayhem that would make a Comanche lose his lunch.

A prominent example was Henry V, king of England, who in 1415 led an expeditionary force of six thousand men — five thousand of whom were archers armed with yew longbows — into France. After weeks of marching, the small army was exhausted and starving. On a dreary fall day they finally encountered a French army of thirty thousand at Agincourt. Henry led his nervous men in prayer, knelt to kiss the ground — symbolizing his willingness to return to the earth — then reminded his men of the French promise to hack the fingers from the right hand of captured archers. With this encouragement he deployed his men for battle. The host of armored French knights charged, their banners snapping in the breeze. A shiver snaked through the English lines. When the enemy was within range, two hundred and fifty yards, the five thousand archers began launching arrows at the rate of one every six seconds. In the first minute of the battle, fifty thousand arrows arched toward the colorful, glittering French cavalry. The courageous knights rode through the hail of armor-piercing bodkin-pointed arrows which buried themselves to the feathers in screaming men and frenzied horses. Some of the surviving cavalry actually made it to the English lines before falling to the whistling death of the arrows. The French infantry, packed shoulder to shoulder, then charged across the casualty-littered battleground as the English archers flung volley after volley into the advancing mass of men. That charge, too, was halted, and toward the end of the encounter the longbowmen stood on heaps of dead to shoot their arrows. The three-hour battle at Agincourt crushed the French army, which lost a total of ten thousand men.

The English liked to say that their country was built with the longbow, but when they weren't using it against outsiders they also turned it against each other. In 1461, during the War of the Roses, English nobles squabbled over who would be king. A battle was fought in a howling snowstorm. The two armies began blindly shooting arrows from long distance, but the archers with the strong wind at their backs had greater range. They fired until their arrows were spent, then moved forward to pick up the arrows from the opposing side which had been falling short due to the wind. By early afternoon, more than twenty thousand men had been slain, a bloodbath by any standard.

The history of the bow is a long and gory one, but it seems the invention of gunpowder and gradual improvements in firearms throughout the 1600 and 1700's slowly inhibited the use of the bow in battle, though archery remained popular among the English for long-range target shooting, a stylized form of warfare. As late as our Revolution, desperate for arms and equipment, Benjamin Franklin wrote to General Lee, "I still wish, with you, that pikes could be introduced and I would add bows and arrows: these were good weapons not wisely laid aside."

Such aberrations aside, North America remained a backwater for archery. Anglos would never dream of using such a primitive device for hunting, though it remained the primary weapon among many native "savages" of the continent who used bows in the old pattern of hunting, having not yet become civilized enough to slaughter tens of thousands of their fellows in a single day. But by the middle 1800's, even Indian archery was fading fast, over-run by our millions with increasingly sophisticated weapons...

Though it was still far too strong, I managed to string the new bow. One limb was stiffer, and straighter, than the other. It was this limb I concentrated on with the rasp, making ten or fifteen sweeping strokes on the belly side, then removing the strung bow from the vice and drawing the string a foot or so to flex the wood. Soon, the stronger limb curved in the same graceful arc as its mate. Now the weight could be reduced by rasping wood evenly from the belly of the entire bow.

While taming the obstinate wood with the rasp, I thought of the two unlikely advocates during the last century who saved archery from oblivion. Maurice and Will Thompson were Confederate veterans who returned home to a devastated Georgia after the War of the Rebellion, as it was known in the 1860's. Union carpetbaggers and regulations forbidding former rebels from possessing firearms left them destitute. In desperation, the two brothers headed south for the wilds of Florida. There, they fashioned bows and arrows and for several years reveled in idyllic wildness with only a pirogue for a boat, exploring the Everglades, meeting Indian hunters and the scattered settlers. Their chief delight was in trying to hit birds on the wing — they once shot 98 arrows, lost 77, and killed 16 birds for their cookpot. Pretty fair country shooting, though on another occasion Maurice wrote, "...lost 60 reed arrows and 17 broadheads by this foolishness." They became silent hunters of deer and black bear. Barefoot, they fished through tranquil summer days and weathered spring thunderstorms.

Maurice eventually wrote a few short stories about their adventures which *Harper's Magazine* published in 1877. They proved so popular the articles were collected into a book, *The Witchery of Archery*. Civilized men choosing to live in such a way fascinated the public, and Maurice's book became a sensation. Inspired by the Thompsons, thousands flocked to archery for recreation, though few actually hunted with their weapons. The fledgling American archery soon degenerated into formalized long-range matches for accuracy.

And so it would have remained, hunting with a bow relegated to a primordial memory, except for Ishi…

The limbs of my bow curved evenly now, and the poundage had been reduced close to intended weight with the rasp. To reach final weight, I switched tools and made long strokes with a butcher knife scraper on the inside of the strung bow, each of which peeled free an onionskin-thin layer of wood. The scraper caressed the wood with a rhythmic hiss… hiss…hiss. The bowyer cannot hurry, for down that frustrating path lies broken bows or bows too weak, a subject any wooden bowyer can expound upon in excruciating detail. No, the bowyer must disconnect himself from the modern world in which events on television are neatly wrapped up in one hour, in which "time is money," in which we must be efficient or perish in the marketplace. How long does it take to make a wooden bow? The question is irrelevant — it takes as long as it takes, a most therapeutic Pre-Columbian attitude to adopt in these times. Hiss…hiss…hiss and the bow emerges at its own pace.

At one point after the turn of the century, public opinion held that hunting with a bow was senseless since it couldn't possibly kill game, that the bow was an elegant toy and no more. But an American Indian started a revolution in archery, the reverberations of which are felt to the present day.

In 1911, a true Stone Age man was discovered half-starved and alone in California, the last of his kind in North America. Ishi, as he was called, was the only surviving member of his tribe. The rest of his people, men, women, and children, had been slaughtered over the previous fifty years by killers out for a bounty on Indian scalps. Rather than sending him to a reservation, in a rare burst of common sense the authorities released Ishi to the staff of the Museum of Anthropology at the University of California in San Francisco. At first, the Stone Age brother to the deer may as well have been transported to Mars — no one spoke his language, automobiles crowded the streets, people filled the city, trains and steamships abounded. But at the museum, Ishi quickly accepted his new surroundings and began demonstrating his skills for the curators and tourists: drawing friction fire from two sticks, fashioning fishing spears, rope, obsidian arrowheads, and, most importantly for posterity, bows and arrows, for Ishi was a master bowyer, arrowmaker, and hunter. He became a celebrity, but in an odd way — everyone wanted to see the wildman, to see if he truly was human.

Since he had little immunity to European diseases he was often sick, and became close friends with a doctor who worked at the university, Saxton Pope. Ishi not only taught Dr. Pope some of his language and how to make bows and arrows but how to hunt with the bow, as well. Pope and his friend Arthur Young had been target archers and readers of the Thompson brother's exploits for years and were fascinated with this idea of taking game with a hand-made weapon. Pope and his young son journeyed with Ishi to his old home country where they hunted and fished with prehistoric weapons, a trip which forever hooked the doctor on the romance and effectiveness of the bow. As time passed, the white men marveled at Ishi's gentleness and patience, but most of all at his lack of bitterness toward the acquisitive race which had overwhelmed and destroyed his culture, his family, and his land. They came to know and admire him as a man of rare honesty and integrity.

And then, the disasters which had haunted Ishi's people caught up with him. He contracted tuberculosis in 1916 and over several months his health quickly declined. Dr. Saxton Pope was with his friend at the end, when Ishi told him, "You stay. I go." According to his wishes, Ishi's bow and arrows were cremated with him.

After Ishi's death the white multitudes mourned his passing, knowing that something irreplaceable had been lost. But Ishi's legacy was the bow and arrow, for Saxton Pope and Arthur Young had been instilled with a fascination for archery hunting, and they determined to prove the bow was a viable weapon, even for big game. They conducted some of the most memorable adventures on record. In his book, *Hunting with the Bow and Arrow*, Pope detailed not only his hunts with Ishi, but also how he and Young hunted deer, black bear, mountain lion, and, most impressive of all, grizzlies. In 1920 Pope with his English-style yew longbow and Young with his bois d'arc flatbow traveled to Wyoming on a grizzly hunt. When it was over, they had slain a thousand pound monster, felled by a single arrow from Young's wood bow. The public was impressed with their exploits, but they were far from finished. In 1925 Pope and Young followed in the footsteps of the ancient charioteers of Egypt and journeyed to Africa to test their weapons against lions. They found that while their arrows killed the King of Beasts surely, they did not kill him instantly, and oftentimes were saved from the close-range charge of a wounded lion by the rifles of their guides. Pope's chronicle of the safari, *The Adventurous Bowmen*, stands as a classic of bowhunting literature and Africana. Shortly after returning from Africa and completing the book, Dr. Saxton Pope died suddenly in 1926.

Art Young continued bowhunting with his trademark fearlessness and accuracy — to appease a crowd of disbelievers, he once shot a flying seagull from the deck of a ship at sea. Shortly before his death in the 1930's he taught a young Fred Bear to make and shoot bows. Bear eventually started selling bows commercially to satisfy the demand brought about in large measure by Pope's books. Along with his chief bowyer, Nels Grumley, Bear became one of the leading archery manufacturers in the country during the late 1930's and early 1940's.

Bowyers had been experimenting for some time with bows from thin wood laminations glued together instead of solid wooden staves. This permitted mechanized bowmaking, as flaws in the wood were negated by multiple laminations. During World War II, Frank Eichholtz, one of the leaders in laminated bow manufacture, was working in an aircraft factory when he came across a springy new material, fiberglass. He found that a wooden core backed and faced with this material yielded a quality bow which could conceivably be mass-produced.

Archery was revolutionized.

There were major production problems to be overcome with the manufacturing and gluing of fiberglass. Most were solved by Fred Bear in the early 50's, and he received numerous patents for his innovations. Bear's high character surfaced when he refused to enforce his patents, in effect giving his inventions to the sport of archery, allowing high-quality, low-cost bows to be made on an assembly line. His genius was nevertheless rewarded as he led a fiberglass archery revolution in the 1950's and 60's which made him rich.

Once a tentative foot is placed on the slippery slope of technology, however, there is no turning back. During the early 1970's, compounds — mechanical bows with wheels and cables — swept the archery world. Their high performance greatly increased their range and lent itself to shooting with sights, like a rifle. But before compounds and their attendant paraphernalia were even invented, conservationist Aldo Leopold had prophetically summed up outdoor "leisure" sports, and modern archery in particular, "Gadgets fill the pockets, they dangle from the neck and belt. The overflow fills the auto trunk...the aggregate poundage becomes tonnage."

Longbows were all but abandoned in the rush to compounds. Manufacturers either switched to the new mechanical bows and their accessories or went out of business. It became impossible to find a longbow in an archery store. Wooden bowmakers grew old and left this world one by one...

The bois d'arc stave was bending nicely now, the weight reduced to a comfortable fifty pounds. After shooting it a hundred times or so, I pronounced it a bow and contemplated naming it "Little Sister," after the Elvis tune. To remove any imperfections, the painstaking sanding process began. As a cloud of yellow wood dust rose from the sandpaper, I hoped Old Ishi would be pleased to see the art he loved so much live on, even in such an alien culture as ours.

In our modern world, why would anyone go to so much trouble making such a bow? A good question, one I've asked myself on occasion, especially during the early learning process when bows broke with numbing regularity. But such thoughts faded as the pull of Ishi and Saxton and Arthur, and yes, the bloody English, too, prompted the shaping of another piece of wood. Perhaps the underlying catalyst for that early obsession — it was the fourteenth try, as I recall, which finally held together long enough to launch an arrow — was a life-sized museum diorama seen as a child. The moment was frozen — a buckskin-clad Indian man, artfully hidden in the brush, holding a wooden bow at full draw only a few feet from an unsuspecting deer. The skill required to get that close to a deer...the patient crafting of such a weapon...the woodsmanship involved...these thoughts lit a fuse which smoldered in my subconscious for fifteen years, until finally they compelled me to pick up drawknife and scraper for the first time. I relearned our ancestors' lessons through mistakes and through the old books until finally, perched up in a pecan tree one fall, I used one of my handmade bows to shoot at a doe. Twice. Both arrows missed so badly they didn't even scare her,

but no matter, I was ruined for life. My wife will testify to this once bowseason begins.

But not everyone feels compelled by tradition. I recently spoke with a man who thought compound bows were not only grand, but that overdraws, 300 grain graphite arrows, six-bladed broadheads, laser sights, stabilizer bars filled with hydraulic fluid, and battery operated grip warmers were glorious innovations and anyone who didn't use them was backwards. I suggested, gently, that perhaps archery shouldn't be so easy, that it shouldn't be instantly gratifying, that it would be more satisfying if it took time and effort and struggle. He looked at me askance, and stated positively that mass-produced synthetic bows were good for manufacturers, good for retailers, good for the Gross National Product and anyone who thought otherwise must be some sort of anarchist.

I was secretly pleased, of course.

All of which is not what I started out to say at all...

I had reached a state of bowmaking grace by becoming one with the sandpaper, the bright yellow dust having crept into every pore. After Zen-level sanding through successively finer and finer grits, the bow was perfectly smooth, but another step remained — rubbing the surface with a polished piece of buffalo bone. Found in the sandhills far out on the plains of West Texas, this ancient bone perhaps added medicine — *puha* as the Comanches say — but more importantly compressed and burnished the wood until it shone like a new silver dollar.

With an indelible pen, I wrote *Little Sister* along with the year on one limb. A generous coating of tung oil, a natural finish, was applied, igniting the inherent fire within the yellow wood. Held in the sunlight, the bow now had depth as if you were looking down into the wood — much the same appearance as a tiger's eye stone. It seemed almost magical that a snarly tree trunk could be transformed into such a lovely, and I trusted deadly, weapon. After several coats of tung oil had dried, I would add a leather handle and tufts of otter fur on the string to silence its twang upon release of an arrow.

The bow was finished just in time. The Crow brothers, Paul and Ted, had called and wanted the three of us to try living off of the land down at the ranch (or The Hideout, as they called it). Sounded like another of their infamous adventures, but a week of deer season remained and I wanted to show *Little Sister* to Elvis.

FOUR

S the crimson hemorrhage of dawn spread slowly across the edge of the world I willed it, without success, to hurry. I shivered in the semi-darkness, the Arctic wind darting past as if anxious to be somewhere else. A splash of sound carried from several hundred yards away—turkeys, perhaps, restless on their roost while they waited for the day to begin. Ground Eagles, we called them, for their eyesight.

Twenty minutes before, when I left Paul on a distinct trail on the downwind side of the deer's bedding area, he had whispered, "I'm hungry enough to lick bugs off the front bumper of a Kenworth. Let's kill something."

Now, standing beside another trail a few hundred yards from Paul, I heartily concurred. We waited for Ted to complete his circle around the bedding area and move through it, pushing the deer toward us. At least that was the strategy. The raucous wind made it too cold to stay still for long, and I remembered how difficult it had been to leave the buffalo robe and the fire-warmed rocks under my feet well before daylight. But the aching void of hunger offered the motivation.

Animals regularly kill in order to live and the last time I

checked we're part of the food chain, too, though I was beginning to have some doubts. In three days of caveman living our small store of dried fruit and jerky quickly vanished. In the last twenty-four hours the food chain appeared to have been broken entirely. There had been not a scrap to eat. If this current plan failed, getting the long distance fangs of our arrows into a deer looked hopeless. We had already tried early morning and late evening ambushes and stalking, none of which had gotten any of us a shot. I wished Old Ishi were here to offer a little guidance.

"Here's what we'll do," I had asserted last night, then detailed the plan for today's drive through the bedding area.

"You really think that'll work?" Paul asked, one eyebrow elevated.

"Of course," I lied.

Due in large measure to long-range rifle hunting, we may well have bred a race of super deer that even Ishi would find difficult to out-fox. For over a century, we've continually removed the curious and slow to react. Today many deer, and especially the big guys, adopt the ultimate survival strategy, nocturnalism, bedding down well before daylight and not moving until after dark. This tactic becomes more evident as the season, and rifle hunting pressure, progresses. The deer have adapted to man, and may be more difficult to hunt today than a hundred years ago. Those who see deer only in parks or residential areas might find the idea farfetched, but tame deer, looking for handouts of popcorn and apples and shrubbery, bear as much resemblance to natural, predator-wary deer as tame, soap opera-watching humans have to their wild, nature-attuned ancestors. The starved bowyer shivering in dawn's half-light most definitely belonged in the tame category.

There are no atheists in foxholes, they say, and I would add that there are mighty few in rockshelters. If we had only known how, Paul, Ted, and I would have gladly invoked some Comanche *puha*, performed an elaborate dance, or repeated a chant to send a deer our way this morning. But we remained sadly ignorant on the subject of hunting ritual, since in the modern world, with control of our food supply through domesticated animals and agriculture, we've forgotten the feeling of being dependent upon Nature, of living by skill and luck.

The brothers who accompanied me seemed unfazed, however, no simple matter like starvation was going to dull their verbal darts. They had kept their sense of humor throughout the frozen ordeal, a survival trait often overlooked by anthropologists. When the canoe turned over, the sleet rattled down, the game vanished, the firewood got wet, the mosquitoes swarmed, or the food ran out, tough determination supported by rustic comedy may pull you through. Good lads, Paul and Ted, good company, though their no-prisoners sense of humor occasionally took an odd twist...

Years ago, I had stopped by to pick up Paul for a hunting trip when a man named Peters arrived to inquire about a pickup truck for sale. Though miffed at the delay, Paul took time to show him the truck. Peters walked around it, examined under the hood, kicked tires, and let fly a covey of questions.

"How much?" he finally wanted to know.

Eight hundred, Paul said, which I knew was three hundred more than he'd been asking. But he was growing impatient to leave on our trip.

"That's sorta high," Peters whined, "could you knock a little off?"

Paul thought for a moment, then shook his head sadly, climbed into the pickup, and took off in a billow of dust. He rammed a tree, crumpling one front fender, backed into another tree, bending the tailgate, then jumped out, caved in the driver's door with a foot, and kicked out both headlights.

"There," he said, walking back to a gaping Peters, "that knocked off about three hundred."

Peters stammered something unintelligible for several seconds before declaring, "Y...y...you're crazy!"

"Yep," Paul agreed, "where's my five hundred bucks."

Peters stammered some more, but was so awed that he finally, incredibly, wrote out a check...

On another occasion, half a dozen of us were sighting in our rifles at the range behind Ted's house.

A mutual friend had a new Remington .22, of which he was especially proud, commenting on how well it shot.

Ted examined the weapon closely, then became deadly serious, a dangerous sign. "Mind if I shoot your rifle?"

The friend urged him to go ahead and shoot it, whereupon Ted tossed it to the ground ten yards in front of him, then emptied his own .22 into the new rifle amid a shower of broken pieces.

Ted nodded and offered sagely, "You're right, that shoots pretty good."

That one stammered quite a bit, too, as do most of their victims (though it's only fair to note that the next day Ted bought the man a new rifle). There are plenty more Crow brothers stories, some of which left me stammering, but perhaps you've gotten the idea...

Little Sister was still frost-laced, though the weak sun now hovered above the horizon. I tried wiggling my toes but couldn't feel them. In the past, my hunting wardrobe had been described as sartorial Armageddon, a solid compliment considering my present hodgepodge of buckskin, wool, and fur, all of which was still not enough to keep me warm in the jostling wind.

Ted should be slowly moving through the bedding area. I wondered if Elvis was there—sharp eyes scanning for the slightest movement, radar ears locked onto every sound, nose testing the wind for a molecule of danger, all of which rendered him invulnerable to a stalking hunter, two or four legged. The rut was long over now, and maybe he would be able to recover part of the weight he had lost chasing does and fighting. He'd need the extra reserve of fat if the winds continued streaming down out of the north. I hoped Elvis was there, but I'd be delighted to show my new bow to any deer.

Waiting with my handmade weapon, stomach growling, it was easy imagining how this country once appeared to those who hunted out of necessity—clear rivers, miles of rolling grass and timber, game and predators in the millions, no fences, no roads, no angora goats. Of course, this eco-system was also full of bowhunting, meat-eating, flintknapping, humans.

Early men walked lightly upon the land due to their small numbers. But these hunters, whether in Ice Age Europe, Asia, Africa, or North America, were opportunists—like herons congregating at an evaporating pond—and thought nothing of running a thousand buffalo off of a cliff to obtain enough meat to feed twenty people. Though they had a spiritual kinship with the animals, they also by necessity had a pack mentality and employed any means, fair or foul, to get meat—surrounds, traps, snares, poison, or chasing animals from a precipice or into deep water. A chasm exists between Paleo hunters' reality and modern hunters' notion of fair play and sportsmanship. The quail hunter won't shoot birds on the ground, where he might kill five at one time, instead waiting for them to flush so he can take an infinitely more difficult shot on the wing. The same applies to duck hunters. And dove hunters. The highlight of a bowhunter's season might be a missed shot or a close encounter with no shot at all. There are exceptions to these ideals, of course, carry-overs from the old "if it's meat, then kill it" mentality of the last century, but the modern hunting ethic compels the broad majority of hunters to play by the rules.

Knowing exactly how those ancients felt who ran buffalo off a cliff, I would shatter any such rules now if I could dynamite a deer, as long as enough was left after the explosion to eat...

Movement a hundred yards away drew my attention. After long moments it came again, a small buck sneaking through the brush, his antlers maybe as wide as his ears. He disappeared and no doubt slipped past me in the thick cedars, though his movement showed that Ted was having an effect on the bedded deer.

No longer noticing the cold, I became more alert. But since my train of thought had about three cars on it my mind soon drifted and for some reason settled upon the bows and epic undertakings of childhood. For a youngster, the museum diorama of the Indian bowhunter acting as one with the woods was a strong image, one to be emulated. We chased rabbits with our fiberglass bows in an area now forever buried beneath a thriving mall. When the rabbits refused to cooperate, which was most of the time, we grew bored and invented shooting games, harmless ones at first such as who could shoot the farthest and later more interesting diversions such as shooting arrows straight up to see who would be the first to run—aboriginal "chicken."

Well I remember the earliest attempt at living off of the land, when I was twelve or so. A friend and I left with tent, bedroll, skillets, fishing poles, flashlights, a sack of candy bars, and enough additional gear in the packs that we grunted under the load. We communed with nature for five days, living on Tootsie Rolls and catfish fried in barbeque sauce. The tent leaked in a storm—before it blew down, that is. We threw a wasp-filled hollow log on the fire one night, and I went home with a 102 degree temperature. I should have acted like a normal civilized human and given up this wilderness folly then, maybe taking up something more practical like interpretive dance.

The wilderness had an attraction, though, one I've never been able to ignore for long. Perhaps it's because the problems one encounters are generally amenable to direct action—if you're thirsty you get a drink, if you're hungry you fix something to eat (often after catching or killing it), if you're cold you build a fire, if you're tired you go to sleep. All surmountable, understandable obstacles, unlike some of our modern problems—violence with no reason, diseases with no cure, politicians with no integrity, television preachers with no shame.

The wilderness had its down-side, however. For instance, in a rockshelter if one left out the last of the dried fruit one might awaken to the sound of saber-toothed tigers fighting over it. It turned out to be two half-grown coons, of course, though fighting three feet from one's sleeping head they made a most passable imitation of their extinct carnivorous brethren...

Deer! Two, three, four does, thirty yards away. Even though they were out of range, they dodged among the trees and vanished before I could draw the bow in a desperation shot. Alert as a bird dog on point, I gripped the bow in shaking hands. But the woods were silent now. After ten minutes it was evident no more deer were coming and I started back to Paul, glad to be moving in the cold. He was visible in the distance talking to Ted. When

I walked up, they both wanted to know what happened and I related the tale of missed opportunity.

Paul grimaced. "I had half a dozen does try to take me prisoner."

"What?"

"They ran by on both sides of me, so close I could've tripped one."

"Did you shoot?" I demanded.

"Hell, no, they were all going Mach 3. I couldn't hit one with a shotgun."

"Any bucks?"

Paul and Ted exchanged a quick glance.

"No," Paul said, "and I'm not sure this Ringo even exists."

"You mean Elvis?" I snapped.

Paul tried to smother a grin. "I haven't seen him either."

Though alertly creeping along, Ted said that he hadn't seen a single deer though he pushed at least ten from the bedding area, a testament to their evasive skill.

"What now, Kemo Sabe?" Paul wanted to know.

I just shook my head, for I was about ready to call out for pizza.

In their ancient way, shadows from the firelight danced on the walls of our small rockshelter. We huddled about the late evening fire, for the wind was now an agate-eyed beast, shoving against us, poking its frigid nose down collars and up coat sleeves, trying to grasp us in its eternal embrace.

Like a pack of coyotes, we had hunted hard the rest of the day. Finally, just before dark, we surrounded a jackrabbit in a brush-pile. We wanted that rabbit. We *needed* that rabbit. Ted made a precise shot through a fist-sized opening in the brush to bag our first meal in two days.

Ted (aka Captain Cholesterol) was always the camp cook. As he propped the skinned rabbit above the coals, he declared that he was preparing his specialty, Jackrabbit Surprise. Sounded great, but I was having visions of the chicken fried steak, cream gravy, and hash browns we would inhale on the way home at our favorite roadside eatery, Chateau de Bubba's (and no, I'm not making up this name).

Ted glanced over at me. "Say, would you mind blowing yourself up again?"

Early that morning, a waterlogged rock we had placed to form the firepit exploded from the heat, bowling me over unharmed but stunned. Paul and Ted went to their knees laughing and had been grinning off and on ever since. Clever fellows.

I noticed a small object shining on the ground. Upon picking it up and angling it in the firelight, I found it to be a piece of oddly colored flint, bright purple. It was the color of Alibates flint, though the prehistoric quarry was hundreds of miles northwest out on the plains, a long way from here by foot. The ancient sight along the Canadian River I knew well, and marveled at finding what appeared to be a flake of the distinctive flint here at the Hideout. Leaning down next to the fire, I saw that the flint was the back half of an arrowhead, broken but carefully worked, the hafting notches on the sides visible now. Holding the point in the firelight, it suddenly seemed as though a foggy window to the past had briefly cleared. Like a scarlet handprint on a cave wall, the point said, "I was here."

After trying a little of this caveman living first hand, it was evident that the men who passed before were as intelligent and inventive as we think we are now. Consider a friction fire produced with a hand drill, a difficult skill to master. Did some prehistoric Einstein make this discovery by himself? Or was it a product of experimentation over many generations? Whatever the case, fire on demand was a more useful innovation than airplanes, or computers, or the internal combustion engine. Our present-day riches may be simply explained by culture, and knowledge, accumulating over time. The collective memory grows as each generation passes down its knowledge. Few of us who value regular meals or hot showers would want to permanently live a raw Stone Age existence, though stepping back and forth between the worlds sharpens the pleasures of each...

Ted announced the rabbit was done, and began passing out portions. I placed the broken point in a buckskin pouch hanging by a thong around my neck. The meal was a surprise, all right, the cremated rabbit was surprisingly good, especially considering the alternative.

As we dined, Paul told of how he once shot a rabbit with an arrow and chased it through the brush for ten minutes. When he finally caught it, he discovered it was unharmed, so he let it go and continued searching until he found the one he'd shot. Hunting stories have probably changed little in the last few hundred thousand years.

Deer season was nearly over, and the deer had kicked my butt. Once again. Jackrabbit Surprise wasn't bad, but fresh venison would have been a lot better.

FIVE

THE man's name was Hummingbird, and he rose early, just before sunrise. His band normally slept late in the wintertime, until the sun had begun warming the earth, and today was no exception. He stepped away from the rockshelter with its sleeping figures wrapped in their buffalo robes. Taking a pinch of sage from a buckskin bag, he sprinkled it to the east — toward the flat-topped mesa, Medicine Hill, silhouetted against the sky — while offering thanks for the deer he had taken the evening before.

Though his band had plenty of dried meat, preserved acorns, and prickly pear fruit, the deer was their first fresh meat in four days. The women had given their high tremolo cries of delight last night when he brought in his kill and his scalp prickled at the memory. The womens' approving calls were sounds any man longed to hear.

Chilled now in the clear winter air, Hummingbird returned to the rockshelter. A few of the children were awake, throwing twigs on the banked coals of last night's fires. Hummingbird plucked an arrow from his bobcat-hide quiver and fetched his repair kit, then took a seat on a rock near one of the fires. He twirled the arrow experimentally between his fingers; the turkey tail fletchings were still good — he had carefully cleaned the blood from them last night; the dogwood shaft was intact and straight, even after passing entirely through the deer yesterday; the stone point, however, had snapped off when it struck the two-year-old buck's rib.

As he cut the sinew binding and began unwrapping the broken point, he reflected on the unusual way he had made it. He had found the stone several days' travel up the nearby Blood River, so called for its red color most of the year. The distinctive purple flint had shown in the gravel of a washed-out bank, and when he removed it found that it had already been worked into a point sometime in the past by one of the Ancient Ones. The broken point was unlike any he had ever seen — two fingers wide with fluted channels running the length of both sides — with most of the tip end missing. Knowing it hadn't originated in his country, he wished there was a way to get more of the brightly colored flint and wondered how far it had been carried before he found it. He placed it in his pouch for several moons before deciding that his medicine was strong enough to risk tampering with the Ancient One's magic, and he used the tip of a deer antler to change the shape and chip it into an arrowhead.

With the sinew binding now free, Hummingbird removed the base of the broken point from the notch in the arrowshaft, examined it for a moment, then tossed it into the fire. He emptied the contents of a buckskin bag, a dozen stone arrowheads, into the palm of one hand and chose a shiny dark brown one, made from a flint nodule he had found on a gravel bar in the Blood River. He sat it beside the arrow, then picked up a dried sheet of deer back sinew and pulled a long thread from one edge, which he placed in his mouth to soften.

Some of the women were stirring about, adding sticks to the fires. Two of them stretched the cleaned stomach from his deer into a shallow depression in the sand, filled it with water, then used forked sticks to drop in a couple of fist-sized rocks dug from the coals. The liquid began bubbling and steaming immediately. Other women sliced portions of his deer's hindquarters into small pieces and dumped them into the boiling water to cook for the first meal of the day.

50

Hummingbird reflected that his people were just like their relatives, the deer, who knew exactly where to find each plant in their territory and when it was most edible. His people traveled a large circle as the plants ripened in season, everyone in the band contributing to the well-being of the whole. The men hunted big game — deer, buffalo, antelope, bear, and turkeys in profusion, if the spirits were kind. Women gathered greens like tangy sorrel and wild onions in the spring after rain; in summer the plums and grapes in the bottomlands; cactus fruits on the high ridges in late summer; pecans, walnuts, and acorns along the creeks and rivers in the fall. Children, too, contributed, the girls helping their mothers and the boys hunting small game such as rabbits, squirrels, and armadillos near the camp. Great was the rejoicing when a boy killed his first big animal — he stood by with sacred marks drawn on his face with his quarry's blood while the people ate the food he had provided and praised him. He received not a bite, but it was a day about which every boy dreamed. Even a crippled old man, mauled by one of the great silver bears of the plains, contributed. Every man could make points, arrows, and bows, but the old man was known throughout the tribe for the quality and finish of his weapons. He had, in fact, made Hummingbird's bow, from the thorny Yellow Wood Tree.

Hummingbird tested the chosen point in the notch of the arrowshaft. A bit too tight. With a thin flint blade, he carefully carved slivers from the edge of the notch, until the arrowhead fit perfectly. He knelt by the fire and placed a lump of cedar pitch on a flat rock, which he pushed closer to the flames. He leaned back while waiting for the pitch to melt.

Though his band's territory was large — more than ten days travel stretching from the heavily timbered regions in the east to the open buffalo plains to the west — he considered this area special, for when he was fourteen winters old it was upon Medicine Hill that he had fasted and prayed and become a man. His uncle instructed him for more than a year in the proper way to seek power, and at dawn one summer morning he climbed the mesa to begin.

After placing four carved sticks vertically into the ground at each of the four directions, he sat down in the middle and waited. That first day, his mind raced like a frightened animal, out of control. He thought of the stories men told of seeking power. How a spirit might offer its help but place the burden of taboos on a man for the rest of his life. How terrible fanged demons sometimes appeared. How lightning sometimes struck the hill, rendering a man crazy with the power it bestowed upon him — he could never marry or sit at a fire someone else had started, though he could call the clouds to bring rain and see clearly into the future. When a man fasted in a lonely place no one might predict what spirit, if any, would appear. Afraid, that first night he slept little, alone after dark without the comforting presence of family and friends for the first time in his life.

The second day hunger tormented him, as his uncle foretold. He could think of nothing but food. During the night his cramping stomach and pounding head allowed no sleep. The third day his thoughts slowed and the hunger faded as he surveyed the panorama from his hilltop, and later, as he lay beneath the stars, he could scarcely tell the difference between being asleep or awake.

The fourth day dawned with his mind clear and still like a deep pool of water. He stood and greeted the rising sun, letting it become part of him. Later, he lay on the ground, and felt his heartbeat slow to match that of the earth's. His body melted into the ground and became one with the rocks — he thought perhaps he was dying.

Late that afternoon, a hummingbird buzzed around him, the sound of his wings low, like distant thunder. He could feel the currents from the bird's wings as he circled. The iridescent green hummingbird alighted on a nearby branch and cocked his head, watching the young man for a long time with glittering eyes.

Finally, the bird asked, "Do you know how to hunt?"

At that point, the young man did not consider a bird speaking to him to be at all unusual, but the question was. Everyone knew how to hunt. "You don't eat, or smoke, or lay with a woman. You rub sage or cedar on your body. And then you hunt."

52

The hummingbird smiled and flicked his tail. "That's the way most men hunt. But I will tell you how to become a hunter the people make songs about. You are what you dream, Little Brother, and you must dream of whichever animal you seek. In the future, cleanse your thoughts like at this moment. Open yourself to this dream and become the animal. Walk in his mind, think like he thinks, and you will become him. And then you will be his hunter."

The bird darted into the air and hovered. "This is my gift to you."

And then he was gone...

Hummingbird crumbled charcoal into the melted cedar pitch and stirred it with a stick. Using the stick, he wiped some of the gum-like pitch into the notch of the arrowshaft, then pressed the point down into the notch and smoothed the extra pitch which oozed out. He spun the shaft checking for point alignment, made a slight correction, and spun it again. Satisfied, he pulled the long thread of moistened sinew from his mouth and began winding it around the notches in the point and the arrowshaft, wrapping the excess up the shaft and securing it with a half-hitch. The sinew would shrink as it dried, securely holding the point in place.

He had heard the big gray cranes flying past in the night, the sure sign of wetter, colder weather to come, so he replaced the arrow in the quiver and carried his bow back to the fire. From the repair kit he took a section of hollow reed filled with rendered bear tallow. Setting the bow across his knees, he poured fat from the container onto the belly and began rubbing the smooth wood with both hands, out and then back to the center, over and over again. The bow quickly warmed. His grand-father had told him that the warming was the soul of a bow glowing with the attention when you rubbed grease into it, and that it should receive the treatment often during wet weather.

Hummingbird noticed his son squatted by the fire watching him. The boy would soon be ready to fast and seek power of his own. And when he became a man the traditions and skills for living in this world would be passed down, generation to generation, as they had been from oldest memory.

SIX

N the distance, a flock of crows — obnoxious gang members — screamed a chorus of obscenities at some owl or hawk. I stopped digging and propped a foot on the shovel to listen. Poised between the melancholy edge of winter and the promise of spring, the tranquil air lay gently upon the earth. None of the dormant plants on the ranch had yet budded, though I was anxious to see how much they would regenerate. Wanting to finish planting the sumacs before dark, I ignored the crows and pulled another bare-root seedling from the bag.

In the past two days, I had planted several hundred seedlings, hackberry, sumac, mulberry, and bois d'arc, the first three for deer forage — they grew naturally in the area, though not on the ranch — the last because I had cut a good many bois d'arc trees over the past twenty years for bow staves and wanted to return some for future generations of bowmakers. Perhaps someday a bowyer will cut one and fashion a bow from it, completing the circle.

The local Soil Conservation Service agent had come out last fall and recommended obtaining the bare-root seedlings from the Forest Service to speed the natural dispersal of native plants.

These preferred deer plants would have eventually crept back onto the place anyway, he said, but it might have taken decades. I had studied deer for thirty years and presumed to know something about them, but spent most of an afternoon following him around the ranch while he pointed out dozens of deer foods in the form of unassuming forbs and browse plants, most of which I had never noticed and couldn't name. There was, indeed, much to learn.

Yesterday morning, besides some scattered does, I had seen a bachelor group of bucks, three of them, their posture and movements signaling the fact that they were male though their antlers were long shed here in March. It did not appear Elvis was among them since all three were about the same size. After the aggressiveness of the rut, bucks usually gravitated together into small, comfortable groups, and Elvis, if he lived, was probably hanging around nearby with some of his cronies. I hadn't seen him since his dramatic Thanksgiving appearance in the oat field, and my growing concern was that he had subsequently been shot by a rifle hunter on one of the adjoining ranches. It was ridiculous, admittedly, but I was outraged by the possibility, having come to think of him as mine.

Most bucks occupy a definitive home range and might spend their lives within a couple of square miles, though they are not territorial in the strictest sense. If Elvis was alive, I somehow felt he was still close, tied to the ranch and the surrounding country. Some bucks, especially the younger ones, travel widely during the rut, spurred by inner restlessness which nature used to distribute the species and prevent inbreeding, a curiosity and aggressiveness which causes them to have a higher natural mortality rate than does. Coyotes certainly killed them more often, largely because dominant rutting bucks run the yearling males away from their mothers in the fall. Such a single young buck by himself does not have the predator alert the added eyes and ears of a group offered.

Young bucks seemed more susceptible to another danger, one I had never before considered. Deer normally float over a fence without effort, but in just the eight months since obtaining the ranch I had found four deer hung dead in the fence, three of which were young males. The deer were caught when they attempted to jump the fence and did not clear the top wire with their feet, causing the top two barbed wires to twist around the leg with the grip of a tourniquet. A terrible way to die, hanging upside down by one leg, until shock or thirst or the merciful wandering coyote finally finished the gruesome business. If I ever built or replaced an existing fence the top two wires would be spaced much farther apart, at least a foot, so there would be less chance of snaring a deer.

Deer are hard on fences in other ways, too, as I've watched them, fleeing from my approach, run headlong into a fence and bounce like a tennis ball from a racket, popping staples from fenceposts twenty feet in both directions. I once saw two deer pull an even more ungraceful stunt. While sneaking through thick cedars, I came within thirty yards of two small bucks bedded down. We all saw each other at the same instant. They leaped to their feet, eyes on me, and immediately ran directly into each other, falling in a tangle of dust and legs. They jumped up again and bolted in opposite directions, though I stayed in the spot a good while longer trying to catch my breath from laughing...

I patted the soil around a foot-tall sumac bush, then wiped hands on jeans and tossed the shovel on top of the last bag of seedlings in the back of the jeep. The jeep was my grandfather's, having passed down to me upon his death ten years ago. He was a masterful fisherman and outdoorsman, and I regretted that he never saw this place, for he would have appreciated it.

Or, in his blunt way he might have remarked, "James... (he and my grandmother were the only ones who ever used my full name)...James, there were too durn many goats here. It never will be worth a crap."

Even so, I still wish he could have seen it.

The place was smallish by ranching standards, certainly never big enough to support a family by stockraising for cash. It stood at the northernmost edge of the so-called Hill Country, only a mile from the Colorado River, from the Spanish word for colored, describing the reddish sediment big rains washed down from the plains out west until at times the river looked like thin tomato soup.

Back to the east, San Saba Peak squatted on the horizon, in spite of the lofty name just a low mesa sprinkled with dark cedars. It was a landmark on the old Austin to Ft. Phantom Hill Road, laid out in the 1850's by Robert E. Lee, then a Lt. Colonel in the U.S. Army.

One of my criteria in choosing this place was, perversely, that there be no oil activity in the area, as there was in many parts of Texas. Few endeavors short of strip mining or clear cutting are so harmful to otherwise good land. Seismic crews, drilling rigs, pipelines, brine spills, sterile pad sites, collection stations and assorted other disasters criss-cross the landscape until the combined weight of activity hangs over the disrupted land like a pall. Rural communities suffer almost as badly, with the influx of roughnecks, con-men, pumpers, gamblers, geologists and other vagrant opportunists overwhelming the fabric of a small town.

No, ma'am, I'll pass, and chose a stable place with few people far from such possibilities and temptations. For the money thrown about during an oil strike can be breath-taking, over-riding any small voice in a community which councils moderation. Were I trying to scratch out a living from this rocky ranch, I would likely shed tears of thanksgiving upon signing the mineral lease from the first oil company to make an offer (and likely, too, my attitude toward goats would soften considerably because they are, in truth, interesting, useful animals — in moderation).

No bigger than this ranch was, it contained a great deal of diversity, one reason I was drawn to it from the beginning. A long rectangle running east and west, a little over a square mile altogether, the eastern half consisted of limestone uplands, with thin dark soil over the chalky rock, composed, they say, of the remnants of a sixty million year old reef. Some areas were rougher where the level uplands broke away toward the creek bottom. Liveoak predominated, thick motts of them which kept their tough leaves all winter, though most areas were more open with grasses such as big bluestem and sideoats. A few clumps of elms stood among the oaks, usually in the deeper soil. Small evergreen cedar was scattered throughout (though it was universally referred to here as cedar, it was, in reality, a juniper, a fact known by almost everyone, an odd regional misnomer I can't explain). It could be an invasive dominator of pastures at its worst but offered increasing deer cover for now, though at some point cedar control through bulldozing or controlled burning might well be necessary. I had concentrated most of the seedling planting here, to increase diversity.

The western half was a different soil type entirely, sandy loam and clay, interspersed with rough blocks of tan and pale orange rock, perfect building stone should the need ever arise. Considerably more brush grew on this end of the ranch; Catclaw Acacia with short curved thorns; holly-like agarita which produced small sweet berries beloved by turkeys and rural jellymakers; mesquite, the crooked hardwood occasionally festooned with mistletoe; and oaks, too, though not so much liveoak here as the graceful Spanish oaks and some stocky post oaks, especially around the field on the western edge of the ranch.

The sixteen acres of cultivated land were planted in oats and wheat for wildlife, not for harvest. Due in part to such crops in this country, there are as many deer now as have ever been. Ever. When Columbus landed here five centuries ago, there is estimated to have been between fourteen and twenty-five million whitetailed deer in North America. Now, studies show around twenty million deer living here, from the palmetto swamps of Louisiana to the frozen plains of Alberta, from the hardwood forests of New England to the thorny brushland of South Texas.

At the end of the last century, deer in many areas had been wiped out or forced to the precipice of extinction by unrestricted year-around market killing, similar to what happened to the buffalo. Deer have returned in numbers equal to all-time highs in part because of a series of laws around the turn of the century — paradoxically passed at the urging of hunters — either severely restricting the season in which deer could be taken or allowing no season at all. Deer numbers began increasing rapidly under this protection, as herds with abundant nutrition do what they had evolved to do — expand by about 50% a year; 1.5, 2.25, 3.37, 5, 7.5, 11, 16.5, 25. Since does have twins each year, and sometimes even triplets, within eight years there would be about twenty-five times as many deer as existed in the beginning. Hunting seasons were liberalized as deer numbers increased to prevent them from destroying their habitat and triggering starvation. But a strictly managed harvest alone was not enough to account for the millions upon millions of deer today.

Whitetails thrive on disturbance, anything which breaks up a solid expanse of forest and promotes growth of weeds and new brush, and Lord knows we have disturbed things in the last hundred years. Though a portion of the whitetail's habitat has been destroyed or altered by our ever-expanding industrial civilization, mechanized agriculture has proven most beneficial. Deer numbers, like those of any other animal, are directly determined by nutrition and modern farming has benefited them, and us, by providing a consistent food source. Deer especially relish crops which help tide them over the winter such as alfalfa, wheat, or oats. These crops maintain their food value when most others are dormant. Apples, corn, carrots, beans, peas, soybeans; deer love and benefit from them all in season.

Because of the damage multitudes of deer inflict upon crops, without controlled hunting farmers and ranchers would have no choice but to kill them. To protect their livelihood, some landowners back in the 1940's and 50's ignored the laws and slaughtered hundreds of deer. But today, deer and many other species of wild game have developed economic value in this country. The fees charged for deer hunting provide up to a third of the yearly income on many Texas ranches. A landowner would have to be economically suicidal not to protect and nurture such a valuable resource. That's why farmers now look the other way when they notice an oat field full of deer. Which is not to suggest that every rancher — or hunter for that matter — is a philanthropic manager of his game, as plenty of pig-headedness still abounds, a subject we'll no doubt delve into eventually...

Bulls Creek, named not for the animal but for a tough family which settled along it back in the testy Comanche days, snakes across the northern part of the ranch. The small creek flows from springs above and remains reliable except during droughts, the silky water falling over innumerable rock ledges along its way to the Colorado River. White-barked sycamores keep a tenacious hold against sporadic floods in the gravel bars along the creek. Hundreds of pecans, some draped with grapevines up out of a goat's reach, line the deeper soils of the creek bottom while the similar black walnuts keep to themselves up the side draws. A few bur oaks, which produce golf ball-sized acorns, stretch for the sun under the canopy of the pecans.

In one loop of the creek stand the tallest trees on the place, stately Durand oaks, a tiny island of this relatively rare species. Relics of an earlier age with a wetter, cooler climate, these oaks are relegated to slowly shrinking spotty habitats throughout Central Texas. I have stood pensively in the small grove, contemplating that in a few centuries these trees and others like them would likely be gone forever. They would be still another victim of the bubbling cauldron of nature, always shoving aside species no longer fit for existing conditions and bringing forth new ones to fill empty niches.

Islands of aspen cling to existence in the mountains of the Big

Bend. Pinyon pine grows down close to the Rio Grande, its nearest relatives hundreds of miles away in New Mexico, both part of a vestigial forest which once covered a far greater area. The empty plains of the Llano Estacado in West Texas were once a pine forest. The Sahara Desert was a well-watered grassland and woolly mammoths grazed on what is now the polar ice cap. Glaciers a mile thick at one time covered present-day Chicago. Seashells fossilized in the rocks speak of living oceans sweeping across continents far in the mind-numbing past.

Seventy-five percent of the species alive during the dinosaur era vanished during the Great Extinction, caused, supposedly, by a meteor striking the earth. Ninety-nine percent of all species which have lived throughout history are now gone. Man seems preoccupied today with some of the changes he has wrought and well he should be, but we have yet to inflict a fraction of the disruption caused by the glaciers during the last Ice Age. In The Big Picture it's evident that for a mighty long time the hand of nature has stirred the cauldron lustily...

In comparison, one's efforts to effect a small piece of land seemed pretty dustmote-sized, but one leaned against the jeep in the evening, satisfied with the day's work, nonetheless. Muscles groaned slightly at the new activity, but they would just have to shut up and take it. This was all part of The Plan.

A current of air cooled both sweaty brow and sweat-damp shirt. The cavernous honk of a Sante Fe locomotive, pulling a grade six miles away near Goldthwaite, grew louder, then faded. A quail whistled hoarsely off to one side. The trees glowed from the setting sun's rays as if lit from within, foretelling the coming rush of spring.

Where were you Elvis? Were you still among the living?

SEVEN

UGUST. The screaming sun hung nailed to the heavens, the flat afternoon light producing a glare which seared the retina. I tramped along behind my two sons, Lee and Reed, who seemed oblivious to the physical burden of the triple-digit heat, throwing rocks and chattering with the boundless energy of a couple of pups.

A month had passed since our last visit to the ranch, and we hiked about surveying the effects of a molten wind which had been sweeping up from the Mexican desert for weeks, sucking moisture and life from plants and animals alike. We discovered that the hundreds of bare-root seedlings I planted late last winter had sent up tentative shoots with the earlier spring showers, but withered and died as summer progressed and the rains stopped. It doesn't always rain just because one thinks it should — we haven't received a drop in almost two months. So much for The Plan. Obviously there was a Far Bigger Plan in effect.

We left the jeep at camp and angled cross-country three-quarters of a mile toward a rough draw and one of the few springs on the ranch. During the best of times the spring only trickled a half-gallon per minute from beneath a rock ledge. I was anxious to see if it had survived the current heat and dry spell, extreme even by our liberal Texas standards.

Many of the elms around us conserved moisture by shedding their leaves as if it were fall, the yellow leaves hanging limp from the branches or carpeting the ground. Veterans at surviving harsh conditions, the wily grass withdrew life into the root system, the standing leaves cured like hay.

Lee, fourteen now, stopped in mid-stride to sniff the southwest breeze like a bloodhound.

"Smoke," he declared.

I sniffed too but decades of allergies often left me all but blind in an olfactory sense.

"Smells like cedar," observed Reed, my youngest at eleven.

Lee cut his eyes at me. "Bet Dad can't smell it."

Scanning the horizon, I saw no smoke, only a distant line of clouds to the southwest. The boys galloped off downhill, the slope steeper and rockier now, racing to see who would be first, competing as usual. Tall with broadening shoulders, Lee usually had the advantage in athletic tests, though he had yet to overcome his smaller brother's lethal jump shot. Reed had suffered various abrasions, stitches, and even broken bones over the years trying to keep up, injuries he listed with the pride of dueling scars.

Lee regularly spoke of seeing Elvis. He would spread his hands wide, glance at his younger brother, then pronounce, "Elvis' rack must be this big."

Reed had not seen Elvis' rack, of course. He always countered with his missed shot at a flock of turkeys that same Thanksgiving weekend after the ice storm. Their stories ended in a tie, for now, though I tried to discourage this mild competition between them where hunting was concerned.

Certainly no one ever accused me of being uncompetitive. A geologic age ago taller basketball opponents referred to me as "The Human Elbow." Nowadays, a friendly game of pool volleyball finds me patrolling the net like a shark. I seem to shoot a bow far above normal capabilities in competition. It's not that I like winning as much as I can't stand losing, all of which is healthy —

I guess. But I've become positively allergic to competition in hunting, as when a man outmaneuvers a nice buck and kills him and is quite properly thrilled, only to suffer disappointment later when a friend gets a bigger deer. Using dead deer to bolster ego is bad enough, but too often money enters the competition equation, as well. In a recent case, a Dallas attorney paid twenty thousand dollars for a trophy whitetail head, only to enter it in the record books, claiming the kill for himself. At LBJ State Park in Central Texas a poacher killed a massive buck enclosed in a pen, the antlers no doubt latter sold to the highest clandestine bidder.

Trophy heads often earn legal money — though no less questionable ethically — through hefty endorsements from sporting goods manufacturers. Such money can lead to affronts like the recent case of a man who regularly killed elk in Yellowstone Park, hunted in numerous states without a license, and routinely cut the horns from game only to leave the meat to rot, all in an mad effort to become the most famous, highly endorsed bowhunter in America. When he was caught and charged with multiple game violations, his sponsoring manufacturers of course circled the public relations wagons to distance themselves from the monster they helped create. The temptation of big money continues, as a world record whitetail buck today might well be worth five hundred thousand dollars in endorsements, the corner-cutting temptations of which are self-evident.

The fault lies not with the record keeping agencies, the Boone and Crockett Club for rifle hunters and Pope and Young Club for bowhunters, as they keep track of the size and location of trophy game animals, a most useful conservation tool. Both agencies police their ranks and are quick to expunge a suspicious kill. Multiple record book entries for commercial gain, however, should be a red flag of warning. Perhaps the answer to these aberrations lies in making the record books anonymous. Publish the size, location, and date of each trophy — but not the hunter.

Which brings up Elvis, who would easily make the record books. He may already be in the record books, for all I know, if a hunter on an adjoining ranch was lucky last season...

The sun blared down while cicadas screeched in their mindless monotone. Even a goat would have sense enough to hug the shade in this heat. Wiping a palm across feverish forehead, I hoped there was still water at the spring. If not, then the wildlife which depended on it — not just deer but quail, raccoons, ring-tailed cats, foxes and dozens of others — would naturally migrate toward the remaining water, the creek or windmills on nearby ranches. Any such concentration of animals results in heavy losses to predators and taxes food supply near the water. The creek still barely trickled along where it entered the place, but by the time it wound over almost two miles of sun-baked rock, enough water evaporated so it ceased running. Some of the deeper holes still held water, but on the western end of the ranch the creek had died.

A drought dries up your spirit in the same way, if you care about land, as you watch the clouds and weatherman's radar with increasing depression. You'll develop a permanent squint from gazing at the empty sky in the summertime, and find yourself wondering if it will ever rain again. The oldtimers here seem reluctant to mention the word "drought" in connection with the current weather, as though they fear angering the gods who send rain. These men, made conservative by a lifetime witnessing calamities brought about by fickle weather and man's folly, remained unimpressed with a mere two month dearth of rain, pointing with shaking finger to the "Big" drought of the fifties. For eleven years, from 1946 thru 1956, rains fell short of the county's yearly average of twenty-eight inches, sometimes far short. All of the springs and creeks dried up, then the Colorado River itself stopped running; cattle and goat herds built up and improved by ranchers over lifetimes were sold off into the teeth of a collapsing market; despair and bankruptcy abounded as the denuded land withered under relentless cloudless skies; and wildlife, especially deer, suffered what is known in biologist's par-lance as a "die-off," not a sight for the squeamish.

In the northern part of the country, the depth of snow and plunge of the thermometer set the parameters on wildlife. Here, the limiting factor on deer remains precipitation — if the rains fall heavy and often the vegetation grows lush, if not, it can start resembling the Sahara from a deer's standpoint. As you move across Texas from east to west, rainfall decreases approximately one inch for every twenty-five miles. The hardwood and pine forests which stretch into the state quickly fade, so the trees in this central part of Texas appear stunted in comparison to those back East.

In a hard summer like this one was shaping up to be, weeds which deer preferred have been scarce since shortly after the rains stopped. The deer have turned to browsing on the brush, which was regenerating to some extent in spite of the weather. It seems that even dry brush maintains most of its nutrition, allowing the deer to stay healthy. For now. Two or three years of continued drought, however, and hungry deer would begin killing off the stressed plants. Under such conditions, they turn entire counties into a moonscape, resulting, of course, in wildlife starvation. The die-off seldom occurrs in the summer, when the disaster begins, but in the fall and winter when animals, weakened by the earlier poor forage, sicken and die. I've only witnessed one such wildlife disaster in my lifetime, in the early 70's, when rains were well below average for three years, and hope never to see another. Emaciated deer; mummified fawns and yearlings curled up under a bush; does and bucks staggering or too weak to move at all.

Young fawns and mature bucks seem especially sensitive when parched weather shrinks the habitat's productivity. Fawns die because their growing bodies require more nutrients and bucks because the exertion of the fall rut leaves them with no reserve for the winter. Such stress naturally makes deer more susceptible to disease in addition to the starvation. By the time the Grim Reaper finishes running his scythe through an overpopulated deer herd the numbers can be slashed in half, and these deer, though they survive, must eke out a living on denuded land. After a few years the plants begin recovering, and deer numbers can increase again.

This boom and bust cycle of animals with no predators has been documented again and again over the last century. If it continues unchecked, the long-term productivity of the land plummets for both wildlife and livestock, until the norm looks like a moonscape. The pruning effect of hunting helps dampen valleys and spikes of deer numbers. It seems kinder by far to employ an arrow to kill a deer in six seconds than allow him to slowly die of starvation for six months.

Instead of controlled hunting, a few have demanded that we institute a program of contraception to control the deer population. Though such a measure would cost more than the budget of some countries and be impossible to implement since each doe has to be treated every year, proponents insist on its implementation since they feel hunting is cruel and unnatural. It's difficult, however, to imagine anything more unnatural and manipulative than slathering birth control agents among the millions of deer which inhabit most of North America. Predators have long kept the deer numbers healthy, but I suppose it's difficult for some to acknowledge that man is one of the predators...

The boys arrived at the spring first, naturally, and were peering beneath the rock ledge when I shuffled into the grove of walnut and willow trees. Wobbling to a stop, I welcomed the shade a moment before squatting down. Water. Blessed water. Not much but some, standing in a shallow pool the size of a washtub in the sand. It was just enough for the wildlife which lived in this area — for the present time, anyway — and us, too. Plucking a tin cup from a nearby branch where we always left it, I held it beneath the weak trickle still issuing from the spring. The metal cooled in my hand as the container filled. After draining the cup once, then again, I handed it to Lee and glanced downstream. The spring's runoff normally flowed fifty yards before vanishing into the sand and evaporating into the atmosphere. A small colony of cattails, which usually thrived in ankle deep water, now stood, yellow, in bare dirt.

This remaining water hole was a magnet for animals in the surrounding country. Pockmarks of deer, raccoon, possum, birds, and other traces too old or small to decipher dimpled the sand. The pool of water contained striders and mosquito larvae and even a solitary crawfish, scuttling backwards from the stick Reed poked about.

The fire must be much bigger — or maybe closer — because now even I smelled it. Stepping from beneath the canopy of trees, I noticed the sun casting a pallid yellow light. Stretching from the southwest, a sheet of dirty smoke hung across the sky, the only break in the heavens beyond the line of clouds on the horizon, larger and closer now. The fire appeared to be at least ten miles away, across the Colorado River. Though the wind was light, the dry vegetation could mean trouble for those nearby. Flames would leap through grass, brush, wooden fenceposts, barns, and trees, especially cedar, which burned with oily flame and awesome roar when dry.

"Let's go," I blurted.

Curious, the boys stepped away from the spring, then noticed the smoke.

Reed asked, "Is it coming this way?"

"Maybe," I answered, "but it can't jump the river unless the wind gets up."

"Then where are we going?"

"Back to camp. We'll drive around and see if we can give them a hand with the fire."

Both boy's eyes widened and they scrambled off without a word, thrilled with the prospect of getting to play firemen. I was less elated at the prospect, having helped with a couple of controlled burns and experienced the hours of shoveling, the searing waves of heat which hit you like a fist, the eerie howl when the flames leaped through tall grass or cedar, the sense of unleashed power and danger, even from a small fire. Such controlled fires in areas of fifty acres or so benefited deer by stimulating short-term weed growth while leaving adjacent cover and browse. Pac Hamblen, a bugler in the wildlife conservation parade, regularly burns long strips across his nearby ranch for the deer's benefit. A keen businessman, he runs cattle and hay cutting operations on his place but like many ranchers spends as much time worrying about the welfare of deer, turkey, quail, myriad "varmints," and the log-sized channel catfish in the lake behind his house.

But a fire out of control, like the one across the river appeared to be, sometimes becomes a monster. Several years ago, a trash fire spread with the help of a forty mile an hour wind up near Albany. Before it was extinguished after three days, it covered more than sixty miles, torched three hundred thousand acres, and caused ten million dollars in damage, despite the efforts of firefighters from several states. Afterward, a great many Texas ranchers, rednecks to the bone, had no better sense than to haul trailer-loads of hay into the burned-out area to give away to strangers, generosity which kept many of the Albany ranchers afloat until the grass returned.

In the old free days, purifying fires used to sweep across Central and West Texas with regularity, sometimes burning for hundreds of miles clear up into Kansas before a river or rains stopped them. Judging from their journals, early explorers found runaway campfires nearly as threatening as thirst or Comanches. And the first settlers, living in their dugouts, wrote of scanning the horizon every evening for the glow of a fire, and when they found one praying that the wind didn't shift and bring its destruction.

Lightning-ignited fires burned a given area naturally every five years by some estimates. There was very little brush then and far fewer trees. The fire killed most vegetation except for the quick-growing grass, showing once again that the so-called balance of nature is no balance at all, but a constant ebb and flow. Plants and animals jostle and choke each other out in their competition for food, space, and water. Grass predominated a century ago, adapted to the frequent burns.

Then came more Anglos behind the explorers, hundreds of thousands of them with their fences and livestock — after finally whipping the Comanches and Kiowas, that is. Early overgrazing along with suppression of fires changed the age-old mix. Brush and trees began creeping up out of the creek bottoms and spreading across the grasslands, slowly at first but then at an accelerated rate, a process continuing to the present day. Deer, rare on the old open grasslands with little to eat and no cover, naturally filled the new brushy niche. Even now, deer are expanding their range along with the mesquite, cedar, and prickly pear cactus into areas they never lived before. My grandfather grew up west of

Ft. Worth in the early 1900's and used to say that deer were non-existent then. If someone saw a deer it was really something to talk about — and to shoot. Today, deer are common in the same area.

Environmental ripples which have spread from events a century ago still effect the relationship between man and deer, predator and prey...

The smoke canopy remained, but what captured my attention now was that the earlier clouds on the horizon had built into a respectable bank. A characteristic feature of owning land in this part of the world is that you pin hopes for rain on every cloud, the optimist in you knowing that moisture eventually comes. Sometimes. The clouds to the west and southwest were at least in the right direction, as storms generally moved to the northeast...

"Dad, there's a deer," Reed whispered, pointing.

Four deer, actually, only fifty yards away, their reddish-gold summer coats like liquid amber pouring through the trees. They stopped. All bucks, their antlers still in velvet and not fully developed. A couple of good bucks. The biggest turned his head to stare at us. A huge ten pointer, I saw now, with antlers far wider than his ears.

Reed hissed, "Is that Elvis?"

I could only nod, a simple-minded grin plastered across my face. Elvis and his colleagues stood in the open, watching us, more curious than alarmed. They all seemed to be in excellent condition, in spite of the dry summer, coats slick and sides smooth with fat. After a few seconds, Elvis walked forward with the deliberate movements of a stately bull. The other big buck moved aside to let him pass. There was no doubt in anyone's mind, including ours, about who was The King. The quartet filtered slowly through the trees, then vanished.

Reed glanced at Lee, mentally sticking out his tongue at his older brother, I thought. Lee didn't notice, for once, but stood staring after the bucks.

I wondered what the deer were doing here in the open on one of the higher ridges of the ranch. And then, looking at it from their point of view, the explanation was clear. The elevation and scattered nature of the trees offered far more cooling breeze than the stifling brush of the bottoms. Simple enough, upon reflection, but seeing Elvis here had been a surprise. He would stay with the other bucks until the ancient urge in September made them start rubbing the velvet from their antlers. They would become more pugnacious then, engaging in shoving and sparing matches to re-establish their pecking order and probe for any weakness, aggressiveness which would last through October. And then, after the beginning of November, the first does would go into heat signaling the fire-drill of the fall rut. But we had a ways to go, yet, first we had to put out a blaze across the river...

The clouds had quickly built into a genuine storm now, moving rapidly as they boiled higher and higher toward the afternoon sun. Heavy with moisture, the air became still as a cellar, making the sweat stream down our faces. Lightning darted once through the cloud, then again. Such a dark flashing cloud behind the smear of smoke was positively primordial, like the beginning of the world. We stopped in the shade to watch. For the first time thunder muttered in the distance. Within minutes the storm rumbled like a distant battle. Finally, the cloud drew its curtain across the sun and immediately became darker, more threatening, the lightning sharp and frequent.

Could it be that the lightning is the thought pattern of a storm, somewhat like our own electrical brain impulses? Or maybe the Indians were right, a giant bird lies behind the storm, with lightning flashing from his eyes and winds whirling from his great wings, the young, inexperienced storm birds causing the damage. Somehow, these explanations seem more symmetrical than the modern scientific one of negative ions, electrons, graupel, and stepped leaders. The mighty clouds certainly don't care what mere men call them, so maybe I prefer the Indian explanation, one which leaves intact the wonder.

Perhaps some things are better left as mysteries — where the sandhill cranes go in the fall and where they come from in the spring, when the first bow was made and what genius midwived the idea, why the liveoaks make basketsfull of acorns during some years and not a handful during another, whether or not there's intelligent life out there. For that matter, how do the sandhill cranes find their way, where are the monarch butterflies going when they occasionally pass through on their colorful mass cavalcade, how did the dinosaurs really die? Perhaps we need these mysteries. Yearn for them. Why else would we regularly see Bigfoot, UFO's, the Loch Ness Monster, and Elvis in the flesh strolling down a grocery store isle in Des Moines?

What *is* the storm thinking with all of that electrical activity?

A sudden wind shoved against us and with it came the sharp, uplifting scent of rain. A shaft of water stretched slowly from the bottom of the cloud until it brushed the ground in the distance, hesitated, then connected earth and sky with its life-giving moisture. Lightning streaked overhead, followed instantly by the sound of ripping heavens. I herded the boys not toward camp but to lower ground to avoid any of the storm's stray thoughts.

We stopped in an opening between two hills, the light underside of leaves flashing as the wind whipped the trees around us. A sprinkle swept across us, then another, then dime-sized raindrops driven by the wind pelted us like liquid marbles hurled from the sky. They increased to a torrent, a deluge, immediately soaking us. We huddled from the onslaught at first, but then stretched our arms upward and turned in circles, conducting a wild, spontaneous dance welcoming the sacred rain like savages, like children.

I've often wondered if animals experience such emotions, too, upon viewing magnificent weather, or waterfalls, or the hardwoods in the autumn changing to yellow, orange, and blood red. Biologists deny it, but still I wonder. Once, I was hunting alone further south when an unusual fall monsoon kept me tentbound for days. In the week-long trip I was able to hunt about two hours, as I recall. At last, the sun broke through the clouds and I sloshed outside. After several minutes of basking I noticed an odd sound, a hawk screaming at regular intervals, over and over again. Squinting, I finally found him, making hundred foot roller coaster dives only to soar again to an apex, stall, let out one of the screams, then dive again. For more than thirty minutes I watched, enchanted. The redtail screamed before each swooping dive in what can only be described as joyous freedom after being earthbound for days by the rain. Scientists would scoff at such anthropomorphic sentiments but I recognize joy when I see it.

Now that the rains had come, I would probably lease the place for cattle grazing to one of the local ranchers who had approached me on the subject. The Indiangrass, sideoats, bluestem, and other grasses stood thick and strong after just a year of rest. Since deer seldom eat grass, state wildlife biologists assure me that moderate stocking with cattle promotes the growth of weeds. As part of the lease deal, maybe I could convince the rancher to plant my small field, since he already had tractor and necessary implements nearby. After seeing this dry summer, perhaps I would not plant the entire field to winter crops in September. I might plant half to winter wheat, clover, and vetch and the other half to summer forbs, useful to deer when they were under the most nutritional stress, does nursing fawns and bucks growing antlers...

The storm with its lightning had moved across us to the east, the rain slowing to a steady sprinkle. We slogged campward. The trees had almost visibly relaxed, standing dripping and contented. There was no trace of the fire after such a downpour — perhaps the volunteer firemen had all danced in the rain, too. Tree frogs clicked madly in their way, the sound synonymous with wet weather. The air was cooler against our soaked clothing, raising goosebumps and giving promise of the coming fall. Maybe the stifling heat had finally broken for this summer. Probably not, as it often lasted up until the middle of October.

We returned to the elevation of camp as the sun fell free of the western edge of the cloud and stood dazzling just above the horizon. The rays of the setting sun ignited the anvil-shaped storm with a wild incandescence, its highest portions seething higher as if stretching for the heavens. As the sun melted away, the purple, crimson, and orange light reflecting from the cloud migrated upward.

I always knew it would rain. Eventually. Never a doubt. All summer I've been collecting seeds of white honeysuckle and sophora from nearby roadway ditches, where they thrived. If they flourished along the roads, where livestock and deer left them alone, it stood to reason that deer would utilize them on the ranch. These plants were unavailable through any nursery or forest service, so I'll sprout the seeds in potting soil next spring then transplant them in May. Keep a gentle hand on the tiller of management, that's the ticket; no micro-managed botanical garden here. Just nudge things along then stand aside, letting the myriad plants and animals prosper in their own way. Maybe we can press forward with The Plan, after all.

EIGHT

WHILE wandering across the corrugated surface of the plowed field picking up flint shards, it occurred to me that three hundred generations of men lived and died here at the Hideout. Ice Age hunters, hunters and gatherers, Comanches, outlaws, farmers — every one left their feel on the land, a subtle imprint you couldn't prove in court but can discern, if you are of a certain mind, right at dusk when the first stars appear, or holding a palmful of flint flakes last touched by humans a few thousand years before, or staring into a mound of glowing mesquite coals. At those times the spirits of the Ancient Ones are in my heart if not in my blood.

The variegated flakes I found in the field ranged from thumbnail to fist-sized with a few as thin and delicate as a potato chip, translucent when held up to the sun and the edges occasionally still razor-sharp. A couple of times I've found more than just debris. The broken purple point from the small rockshelter no doubt had a story, if only it could be deciphered. On another occasion when the field had been freshly plowed I happened upon the very tip of a piece of carefully flaked quartzite, clear as bottle glass. Perhaps it had been the tip of an arrowhead, or maybe a spearpoint, broken in some encounter with a woolly rhinocerous or a woolly whitetail. Or perhaps its maker had snapped the tip off during the delicate knapping process, flinging it down with a curse when it broke (it's a little-known fact that clumsy Paleolithic flintknappers actually invented cursing).

These waves of men left their marks like a flooding creek leaves layers of gravel and sand. The earliest traces here were from hunters of the first water, using their flint-tipped spears to slay woolly mammoths, cave bears, and giant bison. Their glorious hunts twelve thousand years ago still resonate like a drum far in the distance, though the actual physical remains are rare, a few broken leaf-shaped spear tips we call Folsom and Clovis, both with the distinctive fluting flakes removed from both faces. In addition to a climate which grew drier and warmer, some scholars maintain those early hunters were so adept they hastened the extinction of the megafauna.

This area of Central Texas remained a haven for hunters and gatherers, even after changes in weather and animal composition. The winters here were relatively mild compared to those farther north. High-quality flint abounded, just waiting for skilled humans to turn it into knives, scrapers, spearpoints, arrowheads, or drills. There was plenty of wood and pure water. And game animals by the millions, an inexhausible supply of protein for Stone Age humans and other predators. For hunters and gatherers, this was a paradise of a kind, a Garden of Eden, and for millennia the people here made legends and babies and songs and festive war on the other scattered tribes.

The bow arrived here in Texas, by the best archaeological estimate, only a couple of thousand years ago, perhaps migrating with a later wave of explorers across the Bering Strait. This new weapon offered greater range and accuracy than the old hand-held spears or atl-atls, and those who came in contact with it quickly learned to make bows of their own. One of these prehistoric bows was found leaning against the wall of a cave farther down the Colorado River. The bow stood as long as I am tall, about seventy-five inches, its maker apparently choosing hickory or pecan, though the wood was so old and covered with tiny cracks that it was difficult to be certain. The bow's lower tip was eaten away due to long contact with the cave's floor. Tiny tool marks from flint scrapers were still visible on the surface of the carefully worked wood and the grip area showed discoloration from long use. I held the bow as had its maker long before, lightly running my fingers over the ancient tool marks while feeling the spirit of a fellow bowyer across the centuries.

Why did the owner prop his bow against the wall of the cavern and walk away, never to return? Was he sick? Injured in some way? Suddenly overrun by an enemy tribe? Or perhaps he was buried deeper in the cave and his bow left by friends and relatives for him to use in the afterlife? Only the most desperate circumstances could have led to the bow's abandonment, and one wishes it could speak for a few seconds to reveal the centuries-old secret...

Such prehistoric puzzles tantalize, but the people left no written records. True record-keepers arrived just five hundred years ago, starting with Columbus' voyage. But along with the scribes, the invaders also brought change as cataclysmic for the hunter/gatherer's venerable way of life as the meteor strike had been to the dinosaurs.

The Spanish invaders from the Old World, after making short work of the Aztecs and appropriating the mineral wealth of Mexico, slowly expanded their empire and began poking out north into the wilderness looking for even more gold. In 1541, Coronado's expedition, fresh from subduing the Pueblo Indians of New Mexico, crept north and east searching for the fabled golden city of Quivira. On the plains of the Texas panhandle, Castaneda, chronicler of the expedition, wrote about the natives they encountered, "these Indians subsist entirely on cattle (buffalo)...They are a gentle people, not cruel, faithful in their friendship..." This description would have astounded any Spaniard of a later era who would know these people as Comanches.

Though the Spanish conquistadors discovered no gold, what they found was far more precious, though few of them realized it. When Mendoza explored part of the nearby Colorado River in 1683 he wrote, "The bottom lands of the river are luxuriant, with plants bearing nuts, grapes, mulberries, and many groves of plums; with much game, wild hens, and a variety of animals such as bear, deer, and antelopes. The number of buffalo is so great that only the divine Majesty is able to count them."

The Spanish found no precious metals in Texas, though nearly every county, including this one, has its legends of "twenty jack loads of gold and silver bullion," always buried and abandoned, supposedly, when teamsters were attacked and overwhelmed by Indians. Our modern lottery mentality wishes it so, and a few normally rational people search for the treasure still. The legends may even be true in a case or two, though no one has ever explained why the Spanish would transport mule-loads of gold and silver *into* Texas.

As far as the Indians were concerned, the Spanish had plenty of gold. But it was in the form of vast herds of horses. In the 1600 and 1700's, Comanches quickly converted from the old foot-bound hunting and gathering lifestyle Coronado encountered to one of horseback masters of their universe. They could now ride down and kill enough buffalo in a day to last an entire year, and energetic people with such newly acquired free time naturally began testing their neighbors, the Mexicans. The Indians found them rich in horses, easily taken because the government feared a revolt and wouldn't allow individuals to own firearms. Large sections of northern Mexico were depopulated and abandoned as the raids intensified. In fact, Comanches used to say that, "the only reason we let some Mexicans live was so they could keep raising horses for Comanches."

Due to such inexorable pressure on their border, in the 1820's the Mexican authorities reluctantly allowed immigration of United States citizens into Texas to act as a buffer against the Comanches. Settlers surged into the state — by 1830, sixteen thousand Americans had emmigrated — and began pushing up near here onto the fringes of the plains, founding the town of Austin and all but taking over the old Spanish mission city of San Antonio. If the Comanches had found the Mexican peasants defenseless to their slashing attacks, the new Texans, or Texicans as they were known then, were another matter entirely. They generally bristled with weapons, and though most of the newcomers rode like old women and some were cowards, others didn't and weren't.

Relations between Texans and Comanches, always distrustful at best, took a disastrous plunge in the late 1830's. Smallpox broke out among the Comanches and their allies, the Kiowas. Half of their people died, and they well understood that the disease had come from the "Tahvos."

Then, in March 1840, a delegation of sixty-five Comanches, men, women, and children, travelled to San Antonio under a truce called by the Texans to exchange prisoners. Twelve Indians leaders were led into a stone building known as the Council House while the others stayed outside in the street. Some of the Comanche boys used their bows to shoot at targets placed by the Tahvo spectators. The mood was jovial, though only one white prisoner, a girl, had been brought in by the Indians. They still held others, and the Texans knew it.

Inside the Council House, the leader of the Texans marched in a company of troops through the back door and ordered the interpreter to inform the outnumbered Comanche leaders that they were being held hostage until every white prisoner had been returned.

The events on that day exhibited monumental ignorance by both sides. The Comanches were accustomed to dealing with unarmed Mexicans and bringing in prisoners one at a time to extract the highest possible ransom. They couldn't yet understand the white-hot rage the Texans felt when their people were taken captive. They would never have brought their women and children to a council if they thought there was a shred of danger.

The Texans as yet had no conception of the way Comanches fought. They never took adult male enemies captive, either killing them as soon as possible or leisurely torturing them to death. They neither asked nor gave quarter. No Comanche man, least of all a prominent leader, would allow himself to be taken prisoner.

The interpreter paled when told the orders he was to translate, blurted out the instructions in Comanche, then bolted through the door. Every Indian man instantly drew a knife and charged the soldiers in the packed room, a move so unexpected the whites were caught completely off guard. The vicious hand to hand melee spilled out into the street as the soldiers opened fire. The Indian women and children joined the fight — one Tahvo onlooker was killed when the headless wooden shaft of a child's arrow buried up to the feathers in his heart. Others were wounded, but the outnumbered Comanches were quickly shot down by the firearms of the soldiers and citizens. All of the Indian men were killed, along with most of the women and children.

After the one-sided Council House fight, as it became known, neither side held any further misconceptions about the state of affairs. It was war to the death for one side or the other.

Though the Hideout was still beyond the edge of the frontier, in what most Texans of the time considered a harrowing wilderness, the conflagration soon swept across this area. A punitive expedition against the Comanches was raised in Austin, a hundred miles southeast of here down the Colorado River (Austin was still the rawest of settlements — an early writer standing downtown on Congress Avenue noted that he could simultaneously hear the clack of billiard balls, the whoop of Indians, and the howling of wolves). The expedition was in retaliation for horse-stealing raids by the Comanches, which were no doubt staged to exact revenge for some relative slain by the Texans, the whole war along the frontier took on that kind of a personal character.

From camp, I can sit gazing west, where a few miles away on the horizon the river loops around a protruding hill. It was here the Tahvos finally found the Comanches at their encampment on Spring Creek, and wished they hadn't. The sixty citizen volunteers along with a dozen Lipan Apache scouts attacked the Comanche camp at dawn one winter morning, expecting their surprise thrust to rout the sleeping village. The Texans quickly found themselves fighting frantically, however, as swarms of enraged warriors rushed to the sound of battle from nearby camps. More than three hundred Comanches finally took position, and one of the settlers later wrote, "We had barely time to form and reload when the enemy charged us in front and on both flanks to within a few steps, which attacks were repeated at short intervals..." The Indians were repulsed, but only just. The Texans were compelled to pull back with their dead and wounded, then suffered the indignity of having to walk all the way back to Austin when the Comanches captured their horses.

Up until this time the fights had been mostly even, with leadership or relative numbers or terrain usually playing the deciding role. The rifles of the settlers were more accurate with greater range than the Indian's bows, but the muzzleloading firearms also offered only one shot and were difficult and slow to reload, especially on horseback. A fairly narrow, esoteric subject, perhaps, but not if you were the one trying desperately to reload while a pack of screeching Comanches raced to see who could be first to splatter your brains. Cool, rifle-armed Texans with cover to fight from usually prevailed against even overwhelming odds. But at that time, no surer way to commit suicide existed than for a party to panic and fire its single-shot rifles all at once, or become entangled in a running horseback fight with the short bows and arrows of the Indians.

Upon hearing a newcomer make a disparaging remark about Indian weapons, as compared to the "romance" of the English longbow, Bigfoot Wallace, a prominent frontierman of the time, replied, "I have seen a great many men in my time spitted with 'dogwood switches,' but I have never heard one of them yet complain of feeling anyways romantic under the circumstances. But the truth is, if you only understood the use of them, you might have a worse weapon than a good bow and arrows; at least, I know they are pretty dangerous in the hands of an Indian."

Then, in the 1840's, the bow suddenly became obsolete with the introduction of repeating pistols. The revolvers were perfect for stirrup to stirrup horseback battle, and the Texans became unafraid to charge a force of Comanches which outnumbered them five to one.

The settlement line inched westward even as the conflict degenerated into a murderous, ephemereal war, with noncombatants from both sides suffering heavily. Comanches swept down with the coming of the full moon, killing men, taking women and children captive, rounding up horses and cattle, then vanishing into the featureless plains by riding day and night, often more than a hundred miles, before dismounting.

Rare is the family with deep roots in Texas who doesn't have a tale from that time, polished with travel down through the generations, and mine is no exception. West of Ft. Worth, my great-great-grandfather was once surprised by Comanches and raced wildly for his dugout house, coattails flapping behind, the howling Indians trying to ride him down. The warriors kept going when he dove through the door, but he found a couple of arrows shot into his coat.

Or, an independent version of the event I've discovered, not the heroic family model, was that he walked into a nearby camp of friendly Indians and accused them of stealing one of his horses. Offended, they chased him all the way home, finally laughing and shooting arrows at him from half-drawn bows. This variation, I'm afraid, has the more metallic ring of truth to it.

Another distant forebear, Caiaphas Ham, was one of those convinced that the Spanish discovered a silver mine on the San Saba River and had hidden wonderful riches thereabout. He and a company of a dozen adventurers, including Jim and Rezin Bowie, set out to find it, but west of here found instead more than a hundred Comanches. Taking refuge in a small grove of liveoaks, the frontiersmen engaged in a ferocious day-long battle known in the history books as the Calf Creek Fight, where half of their number were wounded and one killed. After finally creeping back to the settlements, Jim Bowie went on to martyrdom at the Alamo and the others lost all interest in Spanish silver. But old Caiaphas' faith in the treasure never wavered, and off and on for the rest of his life he roamed Central Texas searching for it. He died just before the turn of the century, at 92, never having found a farthing.

In the 1870's, the Comanches finally straggled into their reservation at Ft. Sill, Oklahoma, overwhelmed by disease, superior numbers (in 1860 there were 600,000 settlers in Texas, against something like 10,000 Comanches), repeating firearms, and exhaustion.

But by that time they had left plenty of stories:

Wilbarger, scalped and left for dead, whose sister in Missouri came to him in a vision and promised to send help, then floated off toward the nearby settlement. There, a Mrs. Hornsby awoke in the night, having seen Wilbarger in a dream, bloody and scalped but leaning against a tree alive. Mrs. Hornsby, a forceful woman, insisted the skeptical men leave before daylight to go to Wilbarger's aid. They found him just as she had foretold, propped against the tree very much alive. Only months later, after Wilbarger had recovered, did he discover that the sister who had saved him had died of the fever in Missouri. Her funeral had been on the very day that he lay wounded and bleeding...

In the early 1860's four hundred Confederate soldiers and volunteers followed an Indian trail southwest of here. Some of them stopped to dig up a fresh Indian grave and plunder the contents against the advice of their comrades. When the soldiers found and attacked the Indian camp the next day, they discovered not Comanches as they'd thought, but nine hundred Kickapoo Indians fleeing the turmoil of Civil War Oklahoma. The Indians all had rifles and knew how to use them, and repulsed the soldiers with extensive losses. Every man who had taken plunder from the Indian grave was killed on the field. One of the wounded that day was from the Bull family, who lived nearby and gave their name to the creek which runs through the Hideout. His life was saved during the fight by one of his compatriots who later said, "I may be the only one in history to carry a Bull from a battlefield..."

Then there was Mose Jackson's family, attacked in their wagon a few miles northwest of here, the parents and two children killed outright and two others, nine and twelve years old, taken captive. A quickly organized force of local settlers and Texas Rangers started in pursuit, which lasted without rest for forty-eight hours. After an exhausting chase of a hundred and fifty miles the Comanches were overtaken and the children recaptured...

So many stories. Frontiersmen who routinely scalped the

Indian dead for trophies. Or the wounded Comanche who was tossed by the settlers into a pen full of hungry hogs. The clash nearby at San Saba Peak, where the Comanches fought until they ran out of arrows, then scattered and escaped. Once the Rangers and Comanches happened to choose the same place along a creek to camp after sunset, neither side discovering the other until they were already mixed together in the darkness. A confused fight erupted which finally left the Texans in smug possession of the camping spot.

The Comanches had their stories, too, Lord knows, and some must have been dandies, though they were mostly lost for only the victors wrote the history. Every creek, every gap in the hills, every spring around here must have had at least one story attached to it, but many are lost now unless some old-timer happened to write them down. The Durand oaks more than likely saw Comanches riding in the full moon driving a herd of stolen horses up the creek, a natural avenue through the surrounding rough hills. But eyes and minds are seldom keen enough to decipher horse tracks more than a century old or hastily piled rock breastworks or healed-over bullet-scarred tree trunks. The stories, history, and graves are still here, though, as surely as air, whether we can see them or not. There are probably some graves here at Hideout among the boulders along the bluffs overlooking the creek, but I haven't looked very hard for them.

I once knew a man, on the plains of the Texas Panhandle, who specialized in finding and excavating old gravesites. Bobby, as he'll be called here, told me about a Comanche grave, that of a two year old girl, containing several dozen silver and copper conchos as well as hundreds of bracelets. He dug up blankets, shirts, rolls of cloth, handfuls of beads, along with saddles, bridles, and bits. One of the saddles had a bullet hole through the girth where the horse had been shot in the heart to provide a mount for the child in the afterlife.

I asked what had happened to the items he discovered.

"Oh, all the artifacts are out in my garage with the skeleton," replied Bobby.

"You still have the child's body?" I asked in disbelief.

"Sure, I have all the stuff spread out around the garage with the bones."

I declined a kind invitation to view the remains and plunder.

"You know, the funniest thing", he confided, "since I dug up that grave I keep imagining I hear a kid crying."

Dubious, I asked for details.

"At first it was just me, then my wife said she heard it and thought maybe our neighbors had grandchildren visiting. I kind of forgot about it until those neighbors asked what was going on. Said they had heard a child crying out in my garage at all hours of the night."

He admitted he was getting a little spooked and asked what he should do.

"If you're worried, put it back," I told him, "put everything back like you found it. Then burn plenty of cedar."

I never spoke to him again but I'm sure he didn't do it. After all, a find like that is worth a lot in terms of dollars. On occasion, I wonder if the child's spirit resides in some dusty museum, or maybe in a millionare's private collection. Maybe she is out on the plains, free and at peace. Or maybe she's in Bobby's garage, still crying softly...

Once the defeated Indians limped onto their reservation, the Tahvos left in control of the Texas frontier should have yearned for peace like a thirsty man yearns for water. But they didn't. Besides settlers and their families, Texas had long been a sanctuary for criminals, deserters, and other rough elements fleeing organized law in the United States. The standard greeting upon meeting a stranger in those days was, "What name are you traveling under?" These outlaws began terrorizing people and stealing livestock, taking up where the Comanches had left off, and honest citizens vowed to put a stop to it, banding together into secret vigilance committees. Vigilantes would advise a criminal that the next sunrise should find him at least a day's travel from his present location. If he disregarded such prudent council, he was hung or, in the idiom of the day, "he became shot." After a time, the lawless ranks were thinned to near nonexistence, either by migration or attrition.

The vigilance committees well served their purpose, but some members had their blood up and refused to disband, using the groups to settle old grievances with neighbors or intimidate adjoining property owners off their land. Others, frightened by night-riders and increasing threats, formed their own groups, and the frontier disolved into bloody chaos, with men ambushed, homes burned, and women and children sometimes killed in the crossfire. This chain of events unfolded in county after county in Central Texas in the 1870's and 80's, the well-intentioned vigilantes almost without exception becoming out-of-control terrorists themselves. Families who had homesteaded the raw country and lived through the harrowing Comanche times abandoned their homes and fled in fear. The insanity fed on itself and continued until the state police force, the Texas Rangers, was summoned. With the steadying presence of the hair-triggered, flint-eyed Rangers, the violence subsided and ceased. An embarrassed silence about the entire matter lasts till the present day in small Texas towns, for scoundrels and murderers and night-riders have descendents, too.

(There should, perhaps, be some deeper meaning to all of this, violence begats violence, maybe, or Homo Homini Lupus — man is wolf unto man. But for sure some of the sharp edges of frontier roughness remain among us today, and not primarily among the rural population, for our modern cities show more and more evidence of the old insanity.)

With the coming of peace, the people were free to focus their energies on subduing the land. Every flat piece of ground along the Colorado and nearby creeks was plowed and planted in cotton, and the field here at Hideout was no exception. For a couple of decades prosperity smiled, but then cotton prices began falling due to overproduction, and the leached-out fields were abandoned to weeds and encroaching brush. The population peaked here about 1910, as did the number of cotton gins, and has been falling ever since.

There are more reminders from that time, initials and dates carved into the face of limestone ledges along the creek by the field. Where are you now J. M., 1918? Len, 1923? Were you the farmer who worked the land? Or hired labor, a cotton picker who stooped all day under a pounding sun, and in the evenings stumbled down to the shade of the big pecans along the creek to splash cool water on dusty, sunburned cheeks and neck? No answers, for the rock carvers who paused here are long dead now, or else shuffled to some rest home, their memories of those days shaded by the descending nightfall of time.

There are ghosts here at the Hideout, all right, violent, gentle, profane, industrious, clever, funny, dishonest. We're all just passing through, but the land remains, shaped a little by our passing, or perhaps more accurately enduring our passing. Maybe in a few thousand years a blue-eyed hunter-gatherer will pause here and finger a fragment of rusted metal, and feel my ghost and wonder.

NINE

FALL in Texas holds a special place in the outdoorsman's heart — tawny afternoons and vivid nights punctuated every week or so by a rowdy cold front, mosquitoes and chiggers and ticks in remission until spring, rattlesnakes mostly hibernated, bucks roaming the woods with antlers gleaming and necks swollen with the rut. Yes, fall is a pleasant time to be afield, and since so much of it passes unnoticed sleeping in an aluminum coffin known as a trailer, Jim Welch and I dragged our cots outside. Flanking the fire, our internal antennas could keep track of wind, temperature, moon phase, and which animals were working the night shift, essential information our deepest consciousness somehow missed knowing, sleeping inside.

Jim and I lay on our mattresses in silence and gazed at the night sky, our breath fogging in the faint firelight. The full moon had set a couple of hours ago, around midnight, leaving a sky alive with stars, some extinct since the dinosaurs, they say, their light just now reaching the earth. In a city, most of the stars were frantic blinking lights of jets circling high above, but here the distant suns were piled one upon the other until the sky glowed with a frozen luminescence.

I searched for the Archer, Sagittarius, but discovered the constellation had already descended below the western horizon. Appropriate enough for us, for my hunt the previous afternoon had also taken a plunge. When I was within sight of my stand, I noticed that my left foot was three inches from a big rattlesnake's head, the owner of which should have been denned up but wasn't. I instantly performed a stunt known in these parts as the Diamondback Shuffle, a brilliant leaping maneuver that cannot be adequately described to anyone who has never actually participated in it. When I related this tale to Jim earlier in the evening, I noticed him trying to suppress a smile. As I described the ensuing battle between Señor Rattlesnake and myself, a mobile conflict which covered a quarter of an acre and took ten minutes, his smile blossomed into laughter. By the time I reached the part about retrieving my scattered binoculars, quiver, arrows, hat, and bow after the fray, Jim was howling and holding his sides, though I failed to find the episode all that humorous.

Despite the taxing nature of the Diamondback Shuffle, the presence of venomous snakes does add a certain stimulation to outdoor activities here. For instance, one earlier warm October morning before daylight, when I was hiking with a flashlight through the knee-tall grass, His Snakeship was very much on my mind. As I ducked under a low-growing liveoak, a turkey roosting six feet overhead awoke, panicked at the light, and took flight through the thick branches. It sounded not unlike a goat tossed from a passing plane landing in the top of the tree. Five minutes later when finally able to breathe again, I headed not for the stand but back to camp for fresh linen...

Jim had not fared much better the afternoon before, waiting on the ground in Frank's brush blind. He explained that at least a dozen does and yearlings had jumped the fence and wandered past his clump of brush until he was surrounded. Just as he was drawing an arrow at a big doe, another deer winded him and snorted, starting a scramble back to the fence. One yearling ducked through the brush of the blind running at full speed and accidentally plowed into Jim at knee-level like a linebacker, sending him sprawling into a prickly algerita holly bush. He showed me the stickers on the back of his coat and even in his pockets, but best of all the deer's scuffed track on his leather quiver, which had been lying on the ground.

"You're supposed to shoot 'em, not take 'em captive," I chuckled.

Jim thought a moment, then rubbed his leg, "Shooting one's easy, you oughta try counting coup on one."

"Maybe that deer was counting coup on you," I suggested.

This coup-counting business would be appropriate. Though Jim's last name, Welch, might seem perfectly Anglo, he is of Indian descent. The original Welch arrived with the Pilgrims in the early 1600's as an indentured servant, spent a couple of years starving under their puritanical tyranny, then skipped town to live with the natives. He finally married into the tribe, thereby spreading his surname through generations of Indians on the East Coast. Jim's father was Seneca and his mother Sioux, so he came by his bowmaking and hunting expertise more directly than most.

He had years of experience hunting deer with a bow in his native Minnesota, and within the first couple of days had accurately evaluated the Hideout from the standpoint of a deer's preferences. His dark eyes didn't miss much in the way of deer sign, a product, he explained, of his early years spent hunting on the reservation, when a kill could make the difference between plenty and hunger. As a skilled bowyer, Jim had convinced most of his bowhunting relatives to switch from compounds back to wooden bows. With his long black hair and freshly completed bois d'arc longbow, which he handled with casual grace, he looked a brother to Ishi and all the other hunters who came before us in this country...

A couple of coyotes began yodeling in their falsetto way down at the bottom of the hill, the wild, pure cry belonging with the star-festooned sky and the fingers of flame caressing the firewood. The nights would be poorer without coyotes, though neighboring ranchers might take heated exception, as thickly populated coyotes could decimate a year's crop of newborn kid goats. There existed, in fact, some smoldering ill will from such ranchers toward absentee landowners, like me, who won't allow state trappers onto their land to clean out the coyotes. The local trapper reminded me of descriptions of the old Texas Rangers, soft-spoken, slight of build, competent, and a deadly shot with any weapon, the kind of man one welcomes for a friend. But as much as I respected him as an individual, I enjoyed the evening music of the coyotes too much to let him trap them. Besides, we were hard-pressed to take enough deer from this place with our bows to keep their population in check, so maybe the coyotes could help crop the surplus.

All of which seemed irrelevant when compared to the question of the larger predators. For the first time, I had heard the howl of a wolf last year while hunting in northern Minnesota with Jim, a primeval sound I would like to hear just once in Texas. Not likely, for the recent reintroduction of these animals to Yellowstone Park raised a bellow of protests from nearby ranchers, and would cause no less of an uproar in Texas. Grizzly bears are long-gone too, the last one killed in 1898 in the Guadalupe Mountains far out west. At the turn of the century an even more unusual carnivore appeared. A jaguar that wandered up from Mexico began killing cattle a few miles from here and scaring the bejeezus out of the cattle's owners. The big cat was finally brought to bay and killed after a hair-raiser of a fight with fifty dogs and a dozen men on horseback.

A couple of other large predators currently fare somewhat better. Black bears, killed off in the past hundred and fifty years, are now making a modest comeback, expanding from the deep woods of East Texas and the western desert of the Big Bend. Mountain lions have always been present though widely scattered, but their numbers seem to be growing judging from the increased sightings across the western two-thirds of the state.

For my part, I would gladly trade a few deer and a steep increase in beef and mohair prices for a chance to see bears and wolves and large cats in the wild, a sentiment which leaves me at odds with ranchers, consumers, and politicians. And, for that matter, with reality...

As if in answer to the coyotes, a tiny screech owl quavered in the distance like a demented horse. He called once, then again, then silence flowed back and gently washed around us.

Jim stirred on his cot. "Have I told you about the Mormon who showed up at one of our dances in South Dakota last summer?"

He related that the missionary in question had walked uninvited into camps and began preaching to the men, women, and children eating their supper. For a couple of hours, he repeatedly stuck his head into tents and tipis and harangued the occupants for their evil ways. Indian people are normally patient and hospitable to a fault, but the pushy zealot persisted until one of Jim's slightly beered-up cousins tired of the rudeness and stepped onto his nearby saddled horse. He dropped a rope loop over the still-ranting missionary and proceeded to trot his mount a couple of miles across the prickly pear-studded prairie.

"The rest of that night," Jim said with his infectious laugh, "us heathens were left alone."

I grinned into the darkness, imagining the missionary was too occupied pulling cactus spines out of his legs to bother anyone.

"You know," Jim mused, "if I barged into a Mormon church, or a Jehovah's Witness church, or a Baptist church and started preaching and trying to convert them to my Indian beliefs, I'd be locked up for twenty years. But they show up at our ceremonials all the time."

"When you rope one of those foaming-at-the-mouth types," I averred, "maybe you guys should spur your horses more."

He snorted and murmured, "that would be an un-Christian thing to do."

A single cricket began chirping softly, the cold air slowing his rhythm like a record at a lower speed. The flames disappeared as the wood was consumed, the stored sun's heat released as pulsing orange coals the color of a sunset, the elemental flame. For a moment the wind shifted, bringing the soft fragrance of cedar smoke.

Once again, we had stayed up most of the night and would likely sleep until the crack of ten tomorrow morning.

Some hunters.

The creek barely trickled through the rocks and over the ledges, the flow weak even after occasional showers earlier in the fall and the relenting of summer's heat. Lacking moisture since spring, the oaks had produced few acorns, normally a staple for deer this time of year. As a result the oat field with its tender green sprigs attracted higher than usual numbers of deer. Earlier in the afternoon I had positioned Jim in a tree covering a favored approach to the field. I waited a couple of hundred yards away on a trail formed by a steep hillside pressing close to the creekbank, funneling any deer through the relatively narrow area.

I smothered a yawn, though we *had* slept until ten o'clock, as predicted. As if in cahoots with us, the wind pushed from the northwest, shuffling the leaves, carrying our scent away from the trails where we expected to see deer. A kingfisher upstream somewhere called with his staccato chuckle. The scent of dust and a far distant skunk drifted on the evening breeze.

Jim had been making a smudge fire of green cedar boughs every afternoon before we went out. He rubbed his new bow carefully in the smoke, but whether for "medicine" or to cover scent he didn't say. Most thoughtful men who hunt exclusively with their bows perform some small ritual such as this, especially when a kill is made, perhaps a natural throwback to our hunting ancestors. Anyone who spends large blocks of time in the woods, much of it lost in quiet contemplation, quickly recognizes the inherent paradox in seeking to kill an animal with whom the hunter might feel a deep kinship, indeed, an animal the hunter might well love. A tangled relationship, one universally recognized by hunting peoples the world over, who might burn tobacco or sage next to a kill when offering thanks to the animal, or leave a small gift to its spirit, or undergo a cleansing sweat bath upon returning, or make fantastic paintings of the animal on cave walls...

As the sun neared the horizon, the temperature drifted down into the forties and the evening procession began. First, a doe and yearling drifted among the mesquite and cedar trees a hundred yards upwind, finally disappearing in the direction of the oat field. I hoped they would pass Jim's stand and offer a shot.

After a ten minutes came a sudden rush of hooves in the leaves and a doe appeared, trotting away from the field instead of toward it, as I expected. Just behind her loped a buck, an eight point with ivory-tipped antlers a little wider than his ears. Heavy muscles rippled under his gray winter coat. The two deer stopped in the clear fifteen yards away but I was off guard, as usual, and was caught facing another opening farther up the trail. Although tempted, I decided to wait for Elvis, who was already late. No way to turn for a shot in any case.

A nice six point buck appeared forty yards away, his concentration focused on the doe. The eight pointer went through a marvelous transformation right before my eyes, his ears flattening and the hair along his neck and back standing upright. Legs stiff, he took a couple of deliberate steps toward the smaller buck, who gave one look, ducked his head and tucked his tail, then dove into the brush in the direction of the oat field. The doe turned, bolting up the trail with the eight-point right behind. They flashed across the opening I faced so fast there was no hope for a shot, even had I wanted one.

Taking a couple of deep breaths and waiting for my predatory juices to quit boiling, I decided that the aggressive display I had just witnessed was as good as a shot at Elvis. Almost. I only hoped Jim was having as much excitement.

At nightfall, I met Jim at the jeep, and even in the darkness could see his smile.

"Ready to do some tracking?" he asked.

"You bet," I replied, heart jumping, "what'd you get?"

"A six point. Came out just before dark."

I couldn't help but laugh quietly.

"What?"

"I'll bet I saw that deer. Watched an eight-point with a doe do a John Wayne imitation on him. Then the six-pointer headed your way."

Flashlights in hand, we started for Jim's stand.

"Where's he hit?" I questioned as we walked.

"Lungs. Arrow penetrated to the feathers. He was really nervous, maybe afraid old John Wayne was after him. It was hard to get the bow drawn and I had to wait till he was past, quartering away."

"How far?"

"'Bout eight yards."

Knowing how difficult drawing on a deer at such close range could be, I considered that Jim had done a masterful job of keeping his composure and waiting until the ideal moment. He was still pretty pumped up, though, judging by his rapid-fire speech and quick steps.

"He was right over here," he said when we reached his stand, pointing with his flashlight beam.

The blood stood out in the light, bright red drops splattered on the grass and leaves. Pulses quickening, we started on the trail, one of us on each side so as not to step where the deer had gone and possibly obscure traces of his passing. Tracking a wounded deer invokes a singular kind of wolf-like intensity, a pure untamed emotion rarely tapped. We uttered not a word as we darted along the trail, an occasional grunt or gesture with the shaft of hand-held light punctuating the search, never moving forward until tracks or more blood were discovered. We paused, unsure, then found where the buck had stopped and turned abruptly toward the creek. As he had gone down the creekbank, the bleeding slowed to an occasional smear on the long grass or a pin-drop on a rock. We stepped across a riffle and stopped again, eyes sweeping the ground in time with the lights. Long minutes passed. Jim squatted, jaw clenched, searching from a different angle. I took a wide step to one side, trying to find where the buck had climbed the bank of the creek. Squinting, I moved the light slowly across the grass.

"Here!" I hissed, leaning forward to finger divots left by the deer's toes near the top of the bank.

From there, we moved forward six inches to a faint smear of blood on a grass stem. Then six more to another track. Then nothing. Jim squatted again, playing his light slowly on every stalk of grass, every leaf, every particle of dirt. He finally ducked and crawled under a low-growing cedar, and when he came out the other side with his face a foot from the ground I knew he was on the track. I circled the bush, playing my light ahead, then stopped when something flashed white. And bright red.

Jim glanced up and I heard him exhale a long breath. "All right," he said softly.

The deer lay on his belly as if he had collapsed in mid-stride, the feathers of the arrow still protruding from his side. Right in the lungs, just as the man said. This was, indeed, the fat six-pointer I had seen earlier. We knelt next to him. Jim placed a hand on his neck, running his fingers through the coarse gray hair of the back and the finer white hair on the underside. After a few moments, he grasped an antler, sadness and exultation chasing each other across his face, the age-old emotions of the hunter.

The buck had only traveled about a hundred yards, but I couldn't say if we had been on the trail three minutes or thirty, time oddly distorted by the intensity of our search. It occurred to me that this was the first deer taken from the ranch in almost two full seasons of hunting. I was almost as thrilled as Jim, if that was possible.

He dipped his fingers in the blood on the deer's side and smeared them down his bow. An appropriate christening, for I knew this was the first kill for the new weapon. Reaching into his quiver, he extracted a clump of dried vegetation and crumbled some by his deer's nose, then flicked his lighter and set the material smoldering. The clean scent of burning sage drifted to me after a moment. Jim washed his hands in the smoke.

Turning, he handed me the remaining bundle of dried sage. "From the Black Hills. Put this in your quiver."

I nodded, relaxed now and at peace with the world. The pent-up tension had evaporated, replaced by a solid contentment.

Ishi would have been proud of us, I think.

TEN

THIN shoals of clouds scurried toward the south, herded along by the latest November cold front. I waited in a chain-on tree stand in one of the Durand Oaks along the creek, seated so high that this stand was "The Skyscraper" to Lee and Reed (in fact, Lee had predicted, no doubt correctly, that sitting in this stand in a thunderstorm would be a religious experience). A steady breeze gently swayed my perch, making me glad for the safety belt attached to a sturdy branch. The cool air currents rattled the remaining yellow leaves like so many tiny cymbals.

Elvis had once again failed to make his scheduled appearance, though I spent every weekend since the beginning of the season, seven in all, waiting for him. Sitting in Frank's brush blind several times yielded sightings of only a few does, yearlings, and a young four-point buck, all of which passed unmolested in my single-minded quest for The King (none of them ran over me, I'm glad to report). I tried the oat field, grunting, rattling antlers to simulate two bucks fighting, and a dozen different stands. Nothing. Well, almost nothing. I had seen numerous deer and a few nice bucks, counting the one I had seen intimidate Jim's deer. One of the bucks I dubbed Son of Elvis, a big eight-pointer with a wide rack. Most deer in this part of the state sported racks about the width of the ears with long tines, so Elvis and his relatives with their wide antlers were genetically distinctive.

Deer patterns and numbers slowly revealed themselves as I spent the fall waiting for Elvis. In fact, I had overheard my wife telling a friend on the phone that I didn't really hunt the deer, but just irritated them. Maybe this would be a new sport, deeritating, where you spend weeks in the woods and never shoot an arrow. Certainly I had honed it to an art.

Lee and Reed sat at strategic stands near the field, where I had dropped them off earlier. Maybe the boys would get a chance near such a tempting food source, though their competitive natures might well clash if one of them made a kill. They both had a great deal to learn about the neccessary stealth of bowhunting, lessons which could only be learned through experience: never attempt to draw the bow when a deer was looking in your direction, never try a shot if the deer was at red-alert, wait until he was slightly past, concentrate on a single spot on the deer's side while you surf on an adrenalin tidal wave. All easier said than done, but the boys would discover for themselves that the learning, and difficulty, was what made bowhunting so intriguing.

I had never used The Skyscraper since it was in such an isolated grove of the big trees along the creek. This was a good place to spend the afternoon, however, meditating and enjoying the silent drama of everchanging clouds and wind and light. Since Elvis had evidently left the building, it was easy to unfocus and allow the peace to soak in through the skin. A relaxing place, far from the labor-saving contrivances which serve not to free us, the beepers and modems and faxes which bind us with their hectic insistence. And Amnesty International should investigate Alexander Graham Bell for his invention, a merciless destroyer of tranquility and balanced thought. It takes most of three days to purge such civilization from ones system, three days for the clacking mental machinery to lose its momentum and quiet down until the softer rythm of the wilds could be clearly heard. This was our fourth day here, and time was just beginning to pass with gentle slowness, as time should pass, the antidote to growing old...

A sparrowhawk glided into my tree and landed on a branch five feet away. I was fully camoed, of course, so he didn't notice me. He preened a few moments, shook himself, then gazed fiercely about in his predatory way. The glob of non-descript matter nearby caught his attention and he looked me all over, then noticed my eyes and instantly went to hyper-alert, the tension like a current in his tiny body as he stared into my pupils. With malice aforethought, I blinked at him. Finally realizing that a huge fellow predator was sitting next to him in the tree, he dove from his branch and fell like a stone, spreading his wings at the last second to swoop away a mere two feet from the ground. I could only imagine the stories he'd tell the other sparrowhawks later.

The overall health of a place can be accurately measured by the diversity and numbers of birds, clever creatures quick to abandon poor habitat or move into an improving one. In the beginning, this place had a noticeable lack of birds — some quail, a few songbirds, the rare turkey, a passing buzzard or hawk. Now, after only a year of what I considered to be recovery, quail whistled everywhere, flocks of turkeys made occasional appearances, a pair of redtail hawks was nesting in a dead pecan along the creek (and woe to the wandering teenager with a .22 rifle who I catch shooting one of them), scores of songbirds acted as nature's alarm clock at dawn each morning, and one, a mockingbird, warbled his borrowed fragments of others bird's songs day and night around camp, without rest, it seemed.

The place had a long way to go, but the slowly improving conditions supported more of everything, not just game animals or birds. Spotlight surveys for deer rarely showed less than a dozen racoons at home in the liveoaks and pecans, a shy ring-tailed cat or two, jackrabbits in the open uplands and cottontails in the thick cover, and occasionally the reflected bright yellow from the eyes of a gray fox, bobcat, or coyote. The Hideout was busy and getting busier. Other factors were at work here beyond the simple reduction of livestock competition, of course. Frosts, rainfall, severity of the winter, the acorn crop, the last fire, and for that matter the last real drought. Taken together, these elements were at least showing a heartbeat on the place, as they always will if we don't abuse the land with our tame livestock and stand out of the way for enough time...

A flight of ducks, half a dozen mallards, whistled past at eye level, headed upstream to a deep hole still holding water. Ducks had been migrating through for weeks with the arrival of cooler weather; mallards and pintails and a few wood ducks, along with many others which I didn't recognize. Though I enjoyed watching ducks and marveled at their journey each fall and spring, I didn't study and understand them as would a duck hunter or bird watcher. Only vaguely did I sense the problems facing ducks, the destruction of wetlands with groups such as Ducks Unlimited fighting to purchase and preserve their habitat. In years past, I had read about birders putting up nesting boxes for ospreys and watching a population rebound. The same for duck hunters building nesting boxes for wood ducks. Such habitat preservation is clearly the key, virtually the only key, for wildlife's future — if the habitat becomes available they will do exactly what they have done over millenia, reproduce and fill the niche.

Efforts of hunters and many other conservationists along with carefully controlled seasons and bag limits are clearly working today; deer have expanded to pre-Colombian numbers; turkey and elk have rebounded; just over four hundred nesting pairs of eagles thirty years ago have soared to over ten thousand birds in the lower forty-eight states alone; alligators, once nearly extinct, thrive along the Gulf Coast; hundreds of thousands of buffalo live on ranches and wildlife preserves. Though they would loathe being linked with rigid environmentalism, farmers and ranchers for their own economic survival and that of their children are becoming more and more conservationist in tone and action. The old westward mindset of using land and moving on is now thankfully the exception rather than the inviolate rule. We've learned, at last, that we're perfectly capable of destroying our ranch, our river drainage, our mountain range, our continent, our planet.

But all of this good news stands vulnerable under a waiting

avalanche. An avalanche of us. I'm partial to humans, some of my favorite people are humans, but Lord knows there are plenty of us now. There is copious open space and wildlife today, especially with increasing conservation efforts, but it's hard to see how the wilds of this country can withstand a human population two or three times larger without relegating wildlife to glorified zoos. The habitat damage such a human population would foster will doom the wilds and everything in them worth saving — a little solitude included.

Eventually, of course, in the Bigger Picture of centuries, balance will be restored, as it always has. Hopefully, the balance will come about through conservation and a stable human population. But as much as we wish to believe otherwise, we're still subject to the laws of Nature, and She has very effective though unpleasant ways of dealing with overpopulations of her animals, as deer die-offs, AIDS, and antibiotic-resistant bacteria should have taught us. At least one hopes so, hopes that we haven't become so clever at manipulating the environment that our numbers can continue expanding exponentially until no trace of wildness remains anywhere (researchers are even now frantically working on genetically engineered barley and rye which will ripen in the Arctic). Deepest intuition suggests that we haven't been part of Nature for a long time, and the terrible truth may be that She has turned Her back on us for our insolence and will allow us to multiply unchecked.

Such thoughts come all too easily to a man perched twenty-five feet up an oak tree with a wooden bow clenched in one hand...

The wind died away as the sun plummeted in the west, Venus — the evening star — trailing dutifully along just behind. A sound nearby caught my attention, at once foreign but oddly familiar. It came again, sounding for all the world like a soft belch. Puzzled, I tried placing the noise and then, with electric certainty, I knew. A buck following a doe in heat had grunted within fifty yards. I silently stood up. The trees were thick in front of me. Now I could hear the crisp rhythym of the deer dancing through the fallen leaves. They stopped. Searching for them through the obstructing branches, my breathing grew more ragged by the moment. I willed my hands to stop trembling but they ignored me, as usual. And then the deer were moving again.

A doe dodged into the clear, twenty yards away, headed for the tree where I waited. Behind, herding her like a cutting horse, was a buck with wide dark antlers. The first glimpse told me it was Elvis in the flesh. Panic. Cerebral vaporlock. He and I were suddenly transported into a vacuum, it seemed. All sounds ceased as if I had gone deaf — no birds, no wind, not a whisper while he trotted forward. It was just him and me in the universe. Every hair of his grey winter coat glistened and rippled as he came straight to me. At last, the chance I had been waiting for. I drew the bow and aimed almost between my feet, an awkward position. The wooden arrow with its razor-sharp broadhead darted down, reaching for The King. Then he was past. The arrow quivered in the ground.

Refusing to believe I had missed such a close shot, I whirled and glared around the tree trunk, somehow expecting to see Elvis falter and fall. But he continued, unharmed, following the doe another forty yards. They stopped, glancing about, uncertain what had happened.

Watching him, I was suddenly overcome by an adrenalin-induced madness, wanting him dead. Dead by any means. I wished for a rifle, a grenade launcher, anything that would kill him and put him out of my misery. The irrational longing passed when the two deer turned and cavorted off through the trees.

Wrapping one arm around the trunk, I held on as the shakes grew worse. One thing for sure, I would never die of a mere heart attack after today. If the current red-lined, valve-floating adrenalin flood didn't explode my heart then something else would have to kill me. Small comfort. I sat — trembling, exhaused, spent, defeated. The traitorous arrow stood in the ground below, mocking my feeble efforts at predatorhood.

Sound returned to the vacuum while the shakes slowly subsided to aftershocks. What now? I was sure to catch it from the boys for missing Elvis. Maybe I wouldn't tell them. But there could be no hiding it, the look on my face would betray me.

Knowing there might never be another chance, the image of Elvis disappearing was imprinted on my mind. I had blown the shot, not a new experience in my bowhunting efforts over the years but unforgivable considering so much time and effort. After climbing down from the tree, I shuffled toward camp, leaving the offending arrow untouched where it stood.

ELEVEN

BILLY Don had lived a fruitful life. He had been moderately faithful to his wife, had overgrazed his ranchland less than some, and had only poached on rare occasions when he was certain he wouldn't get caught. So after his untimely death (due to falling asleep in his treestand without a safety belt after an all-night poker game), he stood before St. Peter with anticipation.

"Hmmm...", St. Peter said, looking up from his records, "a bowhunter, I see."

"Yes, Your Eminence," Billy Don said.

St. Peter pursed his lips, "I guess you would prefer accommodations pertaining to the hunt."

"Oh, that would be great, Your Worship!" Billy Don burst out, "maybe a treestand in a pretty spot with a big deer trail under it."

St. Peter stroked his beard, "I think that can be arranged."

He summoned an angel, who took B. Don by the hand, flapped his wings, and began flying away.

"And wear your safety belt this time, you dolt," St. Peter called after them.

The angel flew them over beautiful country, full of hardwoods, rough hills, splashing creeks, and bountiful game.

At last, Billy Don pointed, "How about there?"

The angel nodded, lowering them toward the indicated tree, an ancient oak standing where a bend in the creek pressed within a few yards of a cliff, a perfect game funnel. When he reached the platform in the tree, Billy Don remembered St. Peter's admonition and quickly secured his safety harness. The angel settled on a branch next to him and whispered, "get ready."

B. Don was surprised to find his favorite bow hanging from a hook — a compound with maximum let-off, overdraw, ten sight pins, and a full complement of the latest graphite arrows with modular six-bladed heads. The steady south breeze touched his cheek as he took note of the sun hanging just above the horizon. "Wonderful," he thought, "prime time."

No sooner had he nocked an arrow and clipped his push-button arrow release on the string than the biggest buck he had ever seen, a heavy twelve-pointer with at least a twenty-two inch spread, came trotting along the trail, head down as if he were trailing a doe. Billy Don drew his arrow, too excited by the quickly moving target to even look at his sight pins. To his amazement, since he'd never had much time to practice, the arrow vanished into the deer's side, a precise heart shot. The deer leaped from the trail, bounded twice, staggered, then fell in a heap.

"Did you see that?" shouted Billy Don, shaking a fist, "quick, let's get down and look at him."

"No," said the angel softly, "get ready."

A flock of turkeys, twenty or more, fed across the creek, at least seventy yards away. Though they were out of range, B. Don had never killed a turkey and immediately launched an arrow. It arced through the air and struck the biggest gobbler, dead-center. The bird thrashed about a few seconds before expiring.

"This is wonderful," Billy Don said, as calmly as he could, "let's get down and get 'em and head for camp." He decided this heaven business was great.

"Get another arrow," the angel said.

A bit puzzled, he followed the angel's instructions. A duck hurtled past overhead. Without thinking, Billy Don drew his bow and flung an arrow up through the branches of the tree. The arrow somehow found an opening in the limbs and flew unerringly to the duck, which it transfixed.

"Unbelievable!" he exclaimed, as the duck tumbled to the ground, "Art Young himself couldn't have made that shot!"

"Oh, no," the angel said, "Mr. Young is not..." He stopped, catching himself. "Just get ready."

B. Don reached for another arrow and was surprised to find his quiver once again full. He noticed the sun did not seem to be moving, still hanging just above the horizon.

"Couldn't we get down and stalk a bit," Billy Don suggested, "or try a drive, or something?"

"His Holiness wouldn't allow that. The rules are quite explicit."

A buck, almost as big as the first, came easing down the trail forty yards away. Knowing what the result would be, Billy D. drew and released. The arrow struck the deer perfectly, and he only went a few steps before collapsing.

"Look," Billy Don said, "we have to get down and dress the game."

"No," the angel said, "get ready."

"Exactly how long do I have to keep this up?"

"Forever."

"The hell you say!" exploded Billy Don.

The angel smiled.

TWELVE

THE February sleet had been pecking against the metal skin of the trailer most of the night, so when the sound finally faded my eyes creaked open. Four A.M. The wind hissed softly through the trees outside, but something was out of place. I sat up and peered through the window. Plenty dark. Tossing back the blankets, I fumbled for a flashlight then swung feet down onto linoleum as cold as mausoleum marble. When I shoved open the door the wind leaped inside to nip at my bare arms and chest.

I thumbed the flashlight switch and a shaft of light poked a hole in the night. Snow — whirling in the beam. The flakes had already settled a couple of inches deep on the ground. Slamming the door, I quickly began climbing into heavy wool clothing and pulling on boots and knit cap. A real tracking snow was a delight. You could learn more about the travels of animals in one day of snow than six months on sun-baked dirt and grass. Snowfall accumulations were unusual in this part of the state, though blizzards occasionally swept across the Panhandle, far to the northwest. When precipitation fell here in the winter it usually took the form of ice; only rarely did the cold deepen enough to turn the sleet into snow.

Stumbling outside, I stood in the darkness to allow my eyes to adjust for a few minutes. The flakes had slowed, it seemed, and the wind subsided until the remaining snow filtered straight down. A flake drifted against my cheek but immediately melted, a sharp dot of cold. The full moon up above the clouds somewhere cast an ethereal glow. There was no color, only gray and black and white as if I were seeing the world through a deer's color-blind eyes. I crunched down the hill, planning to follow the creek to read exactly where deer where crossing. Later, if the snow lasted, I would do the same with fences.

I wished now the boys had come with me for the weekend. They would enjoy playing in the snow and tracking, though perhaps not getting up in the middle of the night to do so. Neither of them had fired an arrow the past hunting season, but both still seemed intent on taking a deer with a bow. Since obtaining this place, the only arrow I've fired in anger, so to speak, was the miss at Elvis. In fact, the only deer taken here in two seasons of hunting had been Jim Welch's buck. Perhaps that's why the endeavor is called hunting and not killing.

But we would need to start culling deer next season, probably eight or so to keep their numbers in balance with the food supply. I had passed up shots at twenty or thirty does and small bucks, but to have any hope of culling enough deer with a bow my shooting would have to improve. I'd always been a respectable shot, as long as I wasn't shooting at anything. But when a deer appeared — and especially a deer like Elvis — the old knees began to buckle and my refined shooting form collapsed into spastic incoherence. But I was working on it. I'd been shooting practically every day since missing the Big E and planned to keep practicing the rest of the year. I didn't intend to blow another opportunity — assuming one came. My biggest problem had been consistent placement of the right hand drawing the arrow and bowstring to the corner of my mouth. The slightest deviation of this anchor point threw the arrow off target a great deal at twenty yards. But after solving that I found other difficulties. Concentration has always been touted as the key to shooting well, and mine isn't the best. Certainly that's why I missed Elvis, failing to concentrate and shoot at a tiny spot instead of the entire deer. It finally occurred to me, too, that shooting took place more with eye and mind than with hands and arms, a breakthrough concept which improved my shooting more than any other factor. Frustration remained high, however, as I might shoot three arrows exactly into the target then the next one wouldn't come close. Thankfully, there was still plenty of time to hone my technique before next season.

All of the practice had underlined one point clearly, the chances of missing increased exponentially with distance. Ideally, a bowhunter should be within twenty yards of his target, with ten being far better, though there is such a thing as getting too close, as Jim Welch can testify. At under five yards, a deer can hear your heart beating, and it is almost impossible to draw a bow without spooking him. A couple of times, when lying flat on the ground, I've had deer approach and jump over me, undoubtedly thinking I was a log. Far out in West Texas a couple of years ago, with a hard wind blowing — the wind obliterated scent and sound and the waving trees and grass masked movement — I was easing through the waist-tall grass and broomweed of a mesquite thicket. The bedded deer couldn't detect me under the conditions but neither could I see them, so they almost literally flushed from under my feet, like quail. Though I was within three or four yards of at least a dozen deer that day, they were so quick I never drew an arrow, much less took a shot. On another occasion with a big wind blowing I placed the sneak on a yearling doe bedded against an oak, until finally I was on one side of the tree and she was on the other, three feet away. After careful consideration, I jumped out screaming and threw my hat at her. She exploded into motion and may be running yet. It was refreshing to give a deer a heart attack, for once. Such encounters as these happened only under unusual circumstances — the ultimate problem remained getting close enough for that certain shot.

Hunting magazines occasionally contain articles about killing game at sixty and seventy yards with a bow. These long ranges are possible, I suppose, especially with the modern mechanical bows, though one wonders how many animals the writers hit but failed to find with those irresponsible long shots, animals they neglected to mention in the magazines. Long shots or shots at moving animals lead to the majority of wounded game, but other factors such as deer jumping at the release of an arrow or twigs which deflect the arrow's flight also contribute. In twenty-five years of bowhunting I have lost three wounded deer, bad hits which resulted from the deer jumping when they heard the bowstring twang. My pursuit was abandoned only after hours searching for track or speck of blood. These deer may have recovered or may have died, but if such incidents happened much more often I would probably give up hunting entirely. Fortunately, they don't, primarily because bowhunters operate with such single-minded concentration when following a wounded deer. Years ago, a ranch owner glibly told me not to worry about a wounded doe I had spent half a day slowly trailing on hands and knees. He said I could shoot another or he would kill one for me with his rifle. I acquainted him with the fact that I didn't want just any deer, but the one arrowed fair and square at fifteen yards. And finally found it, too, much to his amazement.

Such extended tracking of a wounded deer happens but rarely, though, because an arrow, for all its grace and elegance, is remarkably lethal when properly placed. If shot in the chest cavity with a one inch wide razor-sharp broadhead, deer rarely traveled more than a hundred yards. A couple of times I have shot deer which jumped as the arrow passed entirely through them, then looked about wondering what happened for several seconds before collapsing.

Clearly, the way to insure a quick clean kill is by getting close. Getting close like… well, like a predator…

The sky was lighter now with dawn's approach, though clumps of stars still peeked through ragged windows between the clouds. Sounds were muffled and subdued, as if reluctant to disturb the stillness; my exhaled breath hung in the air like a translucent ghost. The story of every animal's passage stood recorded in exquisite detail upon the surface of the snow. The meandering trail of a gray fox showed he had hunted for two hundred yards among brushpiles and trees. He surprised a covey of quail where they had weathered the storm under a thick bush, marked by a burst of feathers and a single drop of blood. Wing feathers left clear brush-marks against the snow as the panicked survivors escaped in all directions. A coon's tracks led from the creek to the base of an old pecan tree where he would sleep away the day in a snug hollow. Perhaps sensing that their friend the fox was busy elsewhere, mice had skittered from bush to bush along the surface of the snow. A varmint of unknown origin had snuffled around a walnut tree, leaving no clear tracks. Another coon? Possum? Polar bear? No way to tell.

I had seen half a dozen deer, chuffing with their warning snorts at every bound. Their tracks lay scattered everywhere, like delicate notes of a silent symphony. Several sets of does and yearlings — a medium-sized deer together with one or two smaller ones — rambled from the oat field across the creek toward an open hillside facing east, the warmest spot once the sun came up. And three other deer — two big ones and a bigger one — which I took to be a bachelor group of bucks, though not Elvis and his associates for the tracks were too small. They headed not for the open like the does but for an eighty acre area of thick cedar along the north fence (remember the bedding area where the Crow Brothers and I conducted the abortive deer drive?). Following all the deer had revealed one creek crossing which I knew about and two I didn't.

Given a few days of this snow I could very likely pin Elvis down and discover the place where he vanished every fall and winter. I could find him and form a strategy, instead of employing the previous haphazard approach. But he was two steps ahead of me and had been from the beginning. Frank's brush blind had given that first look at Elvis, though his instinctive avoidance of the main trail hadn't even offered a shot. Later, the grunt tube in the oat field had thrown him a curve and brought him within range, but his luck held and Lee never had a shot. My one chance at him last fall had been an accident, since The Skyscraper was the last place I expected to see him. I wondered how much effect I'd had on him; so far, it seemed I hadn't even been able to irritate him much.

Six weeks of rifle season remained after I shot at Elvis, so all of these mental calisthenics may be moot. He was a trophy any dedicated hunter would be proud of, and even now could be staring down from someone's living room wall. I just hoped if he fell before a rifle that the hunter appreciated him. But Elvis was clever. Clever and lucky, I mused, remembering the missed arrow. He was a survivor and I was confident he outwitted the rifle hunters.

If Elvis was still of this earth, he should be shedding his antlers soon. New ones would begin growing with the lushness and abundance of late spring. At least I hoped this spring would be abundant. Though we had received a few showers, last fall had only been a continuation of the dry summer. It had reached the point that even the old-timers were commenting on the drought. Spring and summer were a time of great nutritional demands by the deer, does pregnant or nursing and bucks with velveted antlers which sometimes grew half an inch a day. If we didn't get some moisture, some real ground-soaking, spring-sustaining moisture, then the deer and all the other wildlife were going to be in trouble. Next fall, I might be reluctantly forced to break out the rifles and reduce the deer population a great deal more than planned...

More tracks along the fence; three deer and farther on a raccoon. The sun was up now, though still hidden by the cloudbank. Snow on the trees began to drip. A four-toed unknown, either bobcat or coyote, had ducked under the bottom wire at a dip in the terrain. I knelt to study the tracks while wishing Old Ishi were here; he would know for sure which animal had passed. He was a master tracker with skills that a house-broken civilized dabbler can scarcely understand. I'll bet he never lost a wounded deer, either.

Upon stepping from the Stone Age and viewing our world, Ishi said that we are sophisticated children — clever but not wise. From this distance he appears to have been a visionary. We spend most of our lives working to pay interest and principal on labor-saving, comfort-inducing devices. Our inventions are cunning, but in the course of a day our eyes rarely fall upon anything we make from start to finish with our own hands, or for that matter by anyone we know. Maybe that's why crafting wooden bows feel so right. They take us back to a time when we still relied on the gods of the hunt for our food, before tame animals and agriculture allowed us to transcend our dependence on the earth and become God…

Are we going, then, to continue throwing these childish rocks at modern civilization? No ma'am, I guess not. Not in this epistle, anyway. Though our very lives have come to depend upon baffling technology I suppose there's no reason for question. Just sit back and enjoy the ride, even if the road at times seems to be angling toward a precipice…

A golden sun had now sailed above the tatters of the remaining cloudbank in the east, and the tap-tapping of drops falling from trees increased to a soft chorus. The snow fractured the direct sunlight into millions of tiny colored pieces and scattered them for my eyes to gather. Wet patches of dirt and rock appeared. The thirsty earth absorbed the moisture, though to make a real difference we needed a Minnesota-style three foot snow instead of three inches.

My feet had been wet and cold for an hour but I hardly noticed; I was contemplating a revelation. The snow revealed the fact that deer invariably jumped a fence at a dip in the terrain, where they couldn't be seen from far away. Sneaky, very sneaky. And if does and average bucks were taking such precautions, then how was Elvis acting? Perhaps I'd had a profound effect on him, after all. He was probably in the grove of trees near The Skyscraper because no humans had been there. He was hard to find not by accident, as I'd thought, but because he was acutely aware of me. Every time I hiked to a stand and back, a scent trail was left behind which he read like tracks in the snow. Every time the jeep started his ears told him exactly where it went, so he was aware that I seldom left the roads. Elvis probably knew me by sight, too, as I did him, for he had no doubt stood unmoving and invisible more than once as I walked past, a ruse I had already caught several does and yearlings using. One doe had even lain down at my approach, making her vanish in the grass, and I wondered how many times Elvis had employed the same tactic. My pattern of hunting from treestands morning and evening was likely second nature to him, and he probably timed his travels to avoid my regular schedule.

In fact, upon reflection, in many ways humans must seem like incredible bumblers to the deer. People only operated in the daytime, had no sense of smell, poor hearing, only saw something if it was moving, rarely left their iron dinosaurs to walk and when they did were clumsy and noisy in the woods. To a wise old buck like Elvis they were easy enough to avoid. I had learned a great deal about him in the past year and a half but now it seemed that he had learned even more about me. I would have to do something he didn't expect. Though having no conception yet what that would be, I decided to keep practicing with *Little Sister*, anyway.

THIRTEEN

HE honeysuckle and sophora seeds I had been hoarding since last summer had sprouted admirably in the potting soil. They would be ready to plant about the first of May, another month or so. I was watering the tiny seedlings when the phone rang. I heard Ted Crow's voice, and he had an idea for another trip.

"Bowhunting for wild hogs," he declared, "in South Texas. Hogs everywhere."

"Hogs?" I repeated, stalling for time. "How big?"

"Oh, they get up to three or four hundred pounds," he answered calmly.

Ted was locally renowned for such ideas. I recalled that several years ago he invented the Crutchmobile, which consisted of a flat-bottomed boat towed far behind a jeep on ice. At fifty miles an hour. Through old gravel pits. He insisted on driving after talking several of us with room-temperature IQ's into riding in the boat. I'm happy to report that everyone involved, including me, healed nicely. But Ted clearly was a dangerous man, and it occurred to me that he might be trying to get even for the earlier survival trip at the Hideout.

"Don't hogs bite?" I asked, considering that a three hundred pound hog's mouth would be the perfect size to fit around a man's thigh. "Don't they have teeth. Long, sharp teeth?"

"Not these hogs," he replied, "this trip will be great."

"Is Paul going?"

"Wouldn't miss it." That surely spelled trouble, but I had been practicing faithfully, and this would be a chance to gauge my skill. In any case *Little Sister* needed a test, never having drawn blood; if she could handle a hog surely she could handle Elvis.

"Alright," I said finally, "I'll go."

Ted was laughing as he hung up.

The mesquite, cactus, and unidentified brush grew so thick the wind could barely blow through them. An hour ago, Ted and I let the four-wheeler coast to a stop and began stalking two hogs who darted across a narrow *sendero*, or road, cleared through the ocean of nightmare vegetation. We advanced most carefully since every branch bristled with thorns.

Though in places the brush was as thick as a Cambodian jungle, with visibility sometimes measured in inches, even where the bushes and cactus and stunted mesquites stood apart few grasses or weeds grew in the sandy soil. This thorny wasteland was deceiving, and must have contained extensive nutrition to support so many animals. Deer and hogs abounded and I'd seen dozens of cottontail rabbits, along with predators, for coyotes and bobcats were numerous, too. Nothing grew over ten feet tall, certainly nothing to climb if a three hundred pound hog began chasing you, like, for instance, the biggest one we had seen cross the *sendero*.

I tried to suppress this thought, but remembered how Paul assured me repeatedly on the long drive down that if a hog bit me he would be glad to sew me up. He even had sterile military surplus sutures, of which he was inordinately proud. What made him think I'd let him within ten miles of me with his curved needle and catgut, I couldn't imagine, but he assured me that he had once read a book on the subject. Wonderful.

After years of exposure to them, I was pretty well immune to the Crow Brothers, but their antics quickly made insomniacs of newcomers (which, come to think of it, was probably why few people showed much enthusiasm for a second trip with them). Their treatment ranged from simple pestering, such as packing sutures in their gear, to more elaborate, industrial-strength torture, such as a walkie talkie hidden under your bed complete with hoodoo shrieks from their end in the middle of the night. They would bear watching, especially if one became hog bit...

Snaking the bow silently through the brush, I noticed that *Little Sister* had darkened considerably in the previous year — from the bright yellow to a brownish-orange. The age of a bois d'arc bow can be roughly gauged by its color, one twenty years old finally turns a lustrous purple-black. Sunlight apparently causes this darkening over time. In fact, bois d'arc is so photosensitive that a negative placed on a smooth, freshly split piece transfers the image to the wood after a day in the sun.

A hog grunted just ahead, less than fifty yards. The slightly sour whiff of pigs drifted to my nostrils but quickly danced away on the capricious wind. If the breeze shifted, and the pigs caught our scent, they would vanish. A glance at Ted fifteen yards to my right showed him grinning and jerking his head forward in a *charge* motion. I waved to let him know he was number one. His grin broadened. We eased forward through the thorny tangle, careful not to make noise but urged on by the knowledge that the hogs were moving and we had to get ahead of them for any hope of a shot.

I had never hunted pigs before this trip, but in the past I had made several calls to places advertising hog hunts. Hunting has its problems these days, and one place I contacted which guaranteed a kill is one of them. After careful questioning it came to light that the "hunt" was conducted in a fifty acre enclosure, with wild hogs bought from trappers turned loose inside. I'm sad to relate that the place was booked up weeks in advance. Certainly nothing illegal was being done, since hogs are not at present considered a game animal and have no season or limit on them.

There's no additional shortage of questionable though entirely legal practices which fall under the heading of "hunting." A friend once hunted for white-winged dove in Mexico, but after watching others kill five and six hundred birds a day he left for home in disgust and didn't pick up a weapon again for several years. I have read of exotic animals such as lions bought from zoos or carnivals then turned loose in an enclosure to be executed — not hunted — by some rifle-armed individual with ethical scurvy.

Last year, more deer were killed during archery-only season with scope-equipped crossbows in Ohio (fortunately one of the few states where they are legal) than with longbows. Hunting over an automatic corn feeder is standard practice here in Texas, and many would find hunting difficult, if not impossible, any other way. Although deer in the central part of the state are at the saturation point, and even more should be killed each year than are currently taken, it would still seem mildly vulgar to shoot a deer who has a mouthful of corn. Some bowhunters disdain using treestands or even camouflage, feeling it weakens the challenge.

I suppose in the end each individual has to examine not only the legalities, which are intricate enough, but at a brain stem level the morality of a particular practice, an entirely different exercise...

Once, when I was thirteen, my father and I traveled to a ranch in the mountains of New Mexico on a mule deer hunt, a trip I had dreamed about for months in advance. Among the other hunters we met upon arrival was one I'll call Fred, since that's not his name. We went out with Fred in a jeep one morning, and discovered his idea of hunting was to drive around looking for deer. I kept wondering when we were going to get out and walk through the spectacular scenery, but was just a kid and kept quiet, eyes open to learn the mystical ways of the hunter. When Fred spotted a deer, whether at fifty yards or five hundred, he would slam on the brakes, leap out, and open up with his rifle. After firing at least a dozen shots at various deer, he managed to hit one, a nice buck, which staggered, then disappeared into the timber at a dead run. Fred pursed his lips and said, "He's not hit too bad.

There's plenty more where that one came from." Whereupon he climbed back into the jeep, started the engine, and proceeded to leave.

My father asserted, "Let's at least go look for a blood trail."

After protests and a brief argument, Fred gave a condescending shrug. We quickly found the blood trail and followed it two hundred yards to the deer, who was shot through the stomach and laying on the ground but very much alive.

"Better shoot him again," advised my father.

"Hell no," Fred snapped, "I'll show you flatlanders how it's done."

He leaned his rifle against a stump, drew his twelve inch knife, and trotted forward. When he grabbed the deer by the antler and leaned down to cut its throat, the deer leaped to his feet. Fred tripped and went down with a strangled shout of alarm, still holding the antler. The lunging deer stepped on him three or four times, eliciting more howls, before jerking free and bolting. More from reflex than anything else I threw up my rifle and fired. The deer went limp in mid-stride and tumbled in a shower of dirt and pine needles.

I'll never forget my father glancing my way and nodding. "Nice shot," he said in a loud voice, "but I think you shot the wrong one..."

A hog grunted softly just ahead, and I could make out indistinct black movement through the tangled vegetation thirty yards away. The hog seemed to be rooting around the edge of a clearing. He moved forward, until I could see his head through an opening.

"They darn sure DO have teeth," I murmured to myself. Long gleaming white ones. I would have to mention the fact to Ted, who had disappeared somewhere to the right. This hog looked pissed and I hadn't done anything to him, yet. The arrow seemed frail and delicate compared to his dark bulk. My shooting had improved with constant practice, but I still was not sure it was up to the task. Maybe we should forget the whole thing while I went to practice for another year or two...

The sound of a revving four-wheeler engine suddenly split the silence. The hogs stiffened. I could hear Paul shouting over the noise of the motor, "Here piggy, piggy, piggy!" He appeared forty yards away, his head seeming to float across the top of the brush. The hogs were having none of this and scattered, breaking branches and grunting. They had been standing along the edge of a road, I realized now, and Paul was returning from his morning hunt and barreled right through the middle of them. He flashed past in the distance and disappeared, having never seen us, his cackling laughter hanging in the air. Though disgusted, I couldn't help feeling some relief, too. I wasn't really mad at that hog, especially with those long teeth.

Ted appeared at my right elbow, a look on his face which would have frozen water. "You need a brother for anything?"

"Not me," I proclaimed, "but maybe tomorrow we should keep Paul with us so he won't screw up our hunting. Put him between us. That way if he has another fit we'll have him in a crossfire."

"Good idea," Ted said.

Low overcast clouds hung in the sky like a worn gray blanket, threatening rain. The wind had cranked around to the north during the night and now pressed steadily against us. Spread out abreast, Paul in the middle as planned, we stalked while watching and listening for any hint of a hog. The brush was full of them this morning, the problem was we didn't know where they were until we were within "excuse me" distance. Slipping through the prickly morass we had already spooked two bunches at ranges well under thirty yards and had yet to see a hog, only hear them crash away.

These hogs were wild and adaptable, bearing about as much resemblance to a domestic pig as a wolf has to a French poodle. In the last few years they have gained a reputation as quite a sporting animal, especially with a bow, and stories of hunters being treed or chewed from ankle to appetite have become common fare for campfire philosophers. Hogs are not considered native to this country (though there is some mild disagreement among archaeologists on this point), having been introduced by

DeSoto during his exploration of Florida in 1539. The first Texas settlers brought domestic hogs here in the early 1800's, turning them loose to fend for themselves and gathering them only once a year in the fall. Natural selection has sharpened these wild hogs, leaving them today lean, aggressive, and alert, a process speeded along by the importation and release of Russian boars in the past fifty years.

Though they can be hunted year around, and predators such as coyotes relish the young, their numbers have multiplied with the spread of brush. With heavy predation and increasing hunting, a sow might be lucky to raise three pigs from a litter of eight. But she can have two or three litters a year, and if you start plugging such numbers into a calculator pretty soon the geometric progression leaves you neck-deep in hogs. Most farmers hate them, as their overnight rooting can leave a wheat field looking as though a bulldozer turned circles all through it. And their rooting makes it almost impossible to fence them in or out.

Wild hogs are good eating, excellent smoked or made into sausage. I hoped to have the opportunity to bite one instead of the other way around...

The group of hogs just ahead were close. Really close. I heard them chewing. I crept forward a few steps and knelt behind a sofa-sized clump of cactus. Something dark moved in the brush to the left-front, then grunted. One leg appeared, along with part of a thick body. No way to tell which part. But the brush was too solid for a shot, anyway. Another grunt, off to the right. More movement, straight ahead ten yards. Where did that one come from? In this brush, hogs were intimidating to the fifth power, but I willed my breathing to steady and, to my amazement, it obeyed.

I remembered Lee's final admonition, "Don't come home as a hog turd, Dad." I remembered my health insurance payment was due. I remembered watching scratchy black and white footage of Art Young running up to a grizzly in Alaska in the early 1920's, of the bear rearing on his hind legs, of Young drawing his bow and driving an arrow into the bear, dead center. Instead of charging and ending Young's budding film career, the grizzly turned and ran a hundred yards before expiring. I remembered reading somewhere that Ishi killed a big black bear with a spear. Maybe so, but Young's and Ishi's hide was not as tender as mine. Not nearly.

The hog ten yards away took a step, revealing part of his shoulder in a narrow opening in the brush. I leaned to the left to find a clear path for the arrow. With shaking hands, I began drawing the bow while noting that the boar's bottom teeth were almost three inches long. And no doubt razor-sharp. Yanking my gaze back to his shoulder, my eyes bore like lasers into a dot of mud stuck to the hair. The right hand touched the anchor point at the corner of my mouth and the arrow was gone. It flickered for an instant in the air then vanished through the hog with a hollow *thwick*.

At that point things began to get real western, as the bronc riders say. The boar bellowed, then here he came. Instinctively, I reached for another arrow. The hog slid to a stop on the other side of my cactus and I froze, still on one knee, staring with the greatest possible interest at his back six feet away. He glared about, popping his teeth, looking for an enemy. No enemies here, just us pale writer-types. I held my breath, not daring to draw another arrow from the back quiver, knowing that at the tiniest sound he might dive through the cactus and land in my lap. No one moved. Stalemate. Mexican standoff as they say in this part of the country.

After about a month, I noticed a gurgle developing in his breathing. A promising sign. A very promising sign, in fact. He staggered, regained his balance for a moment, then collapsed and disappeared. A millimeter at a time, I stood, while finally fitting another arrow to the bowstring. Circling the cactus to the right, I walked like I was treading on Señor Rattlesnake himself.

A hiss twenty feet behind gave me a mild stroke, but it was just Paul, grinning like a possum. We both approached the hog, about a two hundred pound boar, perfect eating size. He was quite deceased, the arrow having zipped entirely through him just behind the shoulder.

Paul pumped my hand. "Good shot. Right in the engine room."

I took a deep breath, trying to compose a coherent thought.

"Have a cigarette," Paul said, lighting one and extending it. He knew perfectly well that I gave up smoking years ago.

"Trust me," he insisted, peering at me and smiling, "you need this. Doctor's orders."

With quivering hands, I placed it between my lips and inhaled deeply. The shakes slowly tapered off as I admired the boar's bridgework. The top and bottom teeth closed across each other like scissors, keeping the edges sharp. Protruding like sabers, the bottom teeth were formidable weapons, capable with one slash of gutting a coyote or crippling a man. If I hunted hogs regularly, I'd no doubt have to start smoking again.

After a few minutes, Ted appeared, having heard the commotion. He stared at the hog and then more closely at me. "Is anybody alright?"

"J...just barely," I sputtered.

Paul grimaced, patting his coat pocket. "You sure you're not hurt? I've got my sutures right here."

Not today, no sir. Not a chance. Stubbing out the cigarette and placing the remains in a pocket, I drew a small sheath knife and knelt to field dress the boar. The memory of this hunt, I realized, would spice the hams and ribs as surely as sage and black pepper and fourteen hours of mesquite smoke. And the meat would be the better for it.

All the practice was paying off, and *Little Sister* was clearly up to any job. The questions I may have had were all answered. Now I just needed one more look at Elvis.

FOURTEEN

THOUGH fall might be the most pleasant time of year in Central Texas with the long-awaited arrival of cooler weather, spring is certainly the most interesting of the seasons, with a hike across a pasture becoming an adventure. The sun rising higher and higher in the sky each day triggered a profusion of blooms as the plants broke free of their dormancy, each adding to the orgy of renewed life.

The first were the plums, braving the remains of winter to send forth their lovely white blossoms in late March. Bush plums grew in scattered clumps in the sandy soil around the oat field on the western edge of the ranch, their flowering a signal of cold weather's final retreat. Tart and full of flavor, we used to pick bush plums every summer for jelly, though we had to be constantly on guard for rattlesnakes, for rats and mice and other small varmints came to eat the plums and the snakes invariably came to thin out their congregation. Of Mexican plum, a small tree, I had only a single example here, clinging to life out of the reach of goats between two boulders on the side of a rough hill. The early flowers had given away the location of others growing under oaks and pecans just over the boundary fences to the west and south, where only cattle grazed.

After the plums came the dogwoods — ours the roughleaved variety — the bushes in the understory along the creeks covered with a silent explosion of white flowers during April. Once you discovered dogwood blossoms, each spring thereafter you saw them everywhere along the roadsides. None grew here on the ranch two years ago, but whether from goat pressure or not I couldn't judge, for the nearest ones I had found stood fifteen miles away along the highway in the northern part of the county. And, yes, I transplanted some, digging the dormant foot-tall root sprouts that first winter and moving them. For the first time they bloomed in a couple of small fenced enclosures, maybe twenty of which all together had been built across the ranch in years past by hunters to keep livestock away from the corn feeders used to lure deer. These fenced areas were now ideal to allow plants such as dogwood to become established and spread by seed and root sprout. Not only did deer browse the leaves and birds love the white berries in the fall, but the straight shoots of resilient wood were used for arrows by Indians from Atlantic to Pacific. Dogwood was one of Ishi's favorite arrow materials, and when the plants begin spreading here it might well be put to that ancient use again.

May saw a profusion of color on this usually parched land, sometimes from suprising sources such as prickly pear cactus, the ferocious plants draped with delicate yellow blossoms. And the wildflowers, if the rains were right, their bright hues splashed across the hillsides: bluebonnets, scarlet Indians paintbrushes, yellow and brown coneflowers (or Mexican hats, for the sombreros they resembled), Indian blankets with their yellow-tipped silver dollar-sized scarlet discs, yellow prickly poppies, low-growing wine cups with the violet petals, and two dozen more, their colors ebbing and flowing and blending with each passing day. (Ted Crow once claimed to have spotted a *flowering imbecelius* — or blooming idiot — but that, perhaps, doesn't belong in this section.)

Some years, due to the timing of frosts or rains or maybe just the caprice of the wildflower gods, plants which normally abound were scarce or non-existent. Such was the case this spring with

132

horsemints, whose purple plumes occasionally dominated pastures. But not now.

The more time I'd spent here at the ranch, the clearer it had become that every plant had its place in the Big Picture, though only a fraction might have value in crass economic terms. Fillaree, an otherwise non-descript forb that early in the spring poked its head through the dried grass, was among the first to feed the hungry deer. Darting from flower to flower, honeybees wallowed in the pollen of our small native vetch, valuable for its ability to capture nitrogen from the air and transfer it to the soil, gradually improving fertility for bees and non-bees alike. A bee-keeper disliked the thorn-clad Hercules' Club bush for the bitter flavor it imparted to his honey, though if said beekeeper happened to have a toothache he might well strip free some of this plant's inner bark and place it on the offending tooth to deaden the pain.

An archer noted the growth of dogwood with satisfaction, and noticed, too, the straight, bow-length sections of elm and cedar trees (I know, it's really juniper, but a bow wood, nonetheless). The rancher favored cedar for fence posts because it resisted rot, though having suppressed fires his entire life might watch the grass-choking evergreens spread across his pastures with dismay. The aesthetic valued cedar for no other reason than its wild sweet aroma on an evening fire. Such a fire, if our aesthetic were practical as well as philosophical, might have been kindled with friction, using the dried flower stalk of the yucca and a bow drill, just as fires had been started around here for the past ten thousand years or so. You might spend some time searching for an intact flower stalk, however, as the deer ate them like ice cream as they emerged this time of year. The yucca was useful in other ways, as well: tough fiber for cordage could be stripped from the spine-tipped leaves and a substitute for soap pounded from the root.

There remained much yet to learn, for there grew hundreds more, some of which I only dimly noticed. Every plant, no matter how humble, contributed to the whole, holding soil in place and trapping water when it fell, feeding the microbe or the millipede or the monster deer or the man, each in his turn...

The intermittent Plan appeared to be back in effect this spring with the return of the rains, which had fallen heavy and often. The creek bounced over its rock ledges once again, the silver thread which held the ranch together. Rain fell most of the day yesterday, in fact. I searched for some sign of Elvis' hoof prints in the soft ground, though it was hard to keep one's mind on tracking with all of the flowers and budding plants tempting investigation.

In the past four days I had planted the honeysuckle and sophora seedlings sprouted from seed, most placed in the small wire enclosures to protect them from deer. Yesterday's rain had come with perfect timing, watering the newly-transplanted seedlings. And to my wonder, the trees planted two winters ago, the hackberry, sumac, mulberry, and bois d'arc, had not died during the previous scorching summer as I'd thought, but were sending up vigorous shoots from ground level. Almost all of them had lived through the drought, it appeared. A few individuals might be lost along the way, of course, but only a minor occurrence in the overall view.

Though the current moist ground was not as revealing as snow, plenty of deer sign still meandered through the verdant grass, which now covered the earth with a protective mantle. The cattle were rotated from pasture to pasture at regular intervals, and this moderate grazing had allowed the grass to rest and recover to its present luxurious state.

(In May, you always dusted powdered sulfur around your legs when walking in tall grass, for this was chigger season. You ignored this procedure only at your uncomfortable peril, for there was nothing quite like having a colony of the tiny mites imbedded in the skin from feet to waist, with their attendant maddening itch. Maybe that's why the Comanches were so ferocious, a few hundred chiggers inside the breechclout would make anyone mad enough to bite splitting wedges in two.)

The mottled carpet of grass was beginning to absorb rainfall like a sponge, allowing it to soak into the ground to reach plant roots and recharge springs, instead of pouring downhill along with its load of topsoil. The topsoil in this part of the state was thin to begin with over the rock, and has been washing away without the protection of grass for a long while now. As early as 1898, a Department of Agriculture representative met with Texas ranchers about overgrazing on their lands. The ranchers drafted and unanimously passed a resolution stating, "That none of us know, or care to know, anything about grasses...we are after getting the most out of them while we can." We're still reaping the aftermath of that particular attitude, and a good many landowners today persist in "getting it while we can."

The almost magical ability of grass to hold rainfall and topsoil was demonstrated several years ago farther out in West Texas, where water is even more precious than here. After the disastrous drought of the early 1950's, several ranchers with large holdings along a branch of the Concho River began bulldozing water-robbing cedar and mesquite. After the brush was cleared, they reseeding native grasses to improve conditions on their denuded land. Having learned the lessons that the brutal drought had taught, they rested the newly reclaimed areas and grazed them gently thereafter. The grazing not only improved, but instead of running off, the rainfall began soaking into the ground, heading inexorably for the shrunken aquifer below. To their amazement, the ranchers found long-dead springs — only vaguely remembered through tales of their grandfathers — beginning to seep and after a couple of years finally concentrate their forces and trickle again down the rocky draws as creeks.

If there is a heaven, surely such men who resurrect extinct springs will find a special place there. By contrast, those who destroy their land and draft resolutions about not caring will hopefully hold a front row seat in the alternative...

I hadn't found Elvis' tracks, though searching for them was a fine excuse to explore after planting the seedlings. Despite using drives, grunt calls, rattling antlers, and trying two dozen different stands on the ranch, all of my intricate plans for taking Elvis had netted me a total of one accidental missed shot. As things stood, he was unkillable. His large blunt-toed tracks found on occasion around the oat field showed he was still in the area, though I didn't think he was using the regular bedding areas of the other deer, eighty acres of thick cedars in the northwest corner of the ranch and the heavy brush on the next place just over my southern boundary. I sensed that he was still here, but the thought had germinated and then grown these past few days that maybe I had been hunting Elvis wrong all of this time. Trying to outmaneuver him with human logic was clearly not the answer. Though I was relatively certain I could beat him three out of four games of chess, he had proven to be the superior tactician here in the woods. I was convinced now that I would have to somehow use deer logic to get inside his mind, would have to start thinking like he thought to get another chance at him.

Where would I be if I were a deer? Where would I be if someone were hunting me? These were the questions I started asking, and came to the conclusion that I would become nocturnal and hide in the daytime where no human ever went, where no human would ever think to look. Though I had traipsed regularly across the ranch the past couple of years, there were still a few places where I had never set foot. After careful contemplation, I winnowed these locations down to three possibilities.

The first two were small mesas with no more than a half acre on top, thickly covered with young liveoaks. An hour ago, my approach across the surrounding open ground had blown a half-dozen bedded deer from both vantage points. Elvis did not appear to be among them, and a careful search of the areas had revealed no trace of him, though deer beds, droppings, and even antler-scarred saplings abounded. The theory was encouraging, though, for the deer seemed concentrated in these tiny areas never breached by humans.

Now, I approached the third and final possibility, a precipitous finger of limestone which forced the creek to make a wide loop around it. Brush-choked, the steepest section was only about fifty yards wide by a hundred long, and though I had hiked all around it had never actually ventured among the boulders because, quite frankly, it seemed a perfect home for Señor Rattlesnake.

I climbed the rocky slope on the back side of the knife-edged ridge, moving slowly to avoid making noise. The perfume from a dozen species of flowers drifted on the warm southerly breeze while a small armada of clouds floated overhead in an ocean of sapphire air. At my approach, grasshoppers rose and clicked away through the knee-high grass. Back to the west where the creek continued its course after looping around the hill, I could see the top of the Durand Oak which held the Skyscraper Stand, and the remembrance of the nearby missed shot last fall encouraged optimism that Elvis might be here.

Confirming the presence of deer without blowing them from the bedding area would prove tricky, as I'd already discovered, and Elvis was wise enough to change locations if I spooked him too badly, even though hunting season was six months away. As if reading my thoughts, a doe, heavy with twin fawns, jumped to her feet fifty yards ahead. She stared a few moments, more indignant than frightened, before trotting down the hill and out of sight among the trees. In a few weeks, her spotted fawns would be born in different places and kept separated until they were mobile enough to avoid predators, nature's way of preventing a coyote or bobcat or fox or coon from killing both helpless offspring at once.

The music of two dozen different birds rose and fell, each straining to out-sing the others. Up the hill, a yellow-breasted meadowlark called with his falling-down-the-stairs whistle, and another answered somewhere behind me. Down along the creek a woodpecker tapped out his secret Morse Code on one of the big pecan trees. An unseen wren called like a ventriloquist from the cedars, first here, then there. A mockingbird seemed perched in every tree, competing to see which one could compose the most outrageous song. Earlier, I had heard the liquid "poit - poit" of turkeys, who had been all but absent during last year's dry spell but had now returned from the Colorado River bottoms...

My eyes had seen something they insisted on telling me more about, so I took two steps backward. I found myself staring at a track in the dirt almost hidden between two clumps of grass. Kneeling, I examined it from a foot away; a deer print big enough to have been made only by Elvis, pressed deeply into the soil from his bulk. When it rained last, which way the wind blew and for how long, when the humidity was highest, whether it had been cloudy or cold or clear, each of these factors leave their marks on the ground and their cumulative effects allow the aging of tracks, a worthwhile skill for someone who spends time in the woods. The clarity of the imprint in question showed it was made after the rain stopped yesterday afternoon but the edges had begun to dry and crack from today's sun, so it was most likely made about daylight.

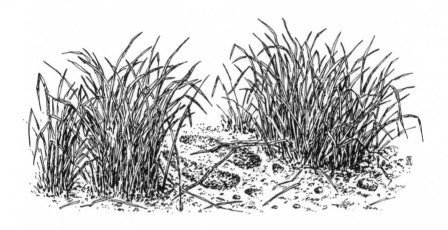

Angling up the hill toward the rocky brush just over the crest, the track suddenly was the key to Elvis' Hideout. Now I wouldn't have to risk blowing him out of his sanctuary and changing his routine, for I knew with certainty where he was. Not as surely as Ishi would have known, perhaps, if examining the same information, but I knew, nevertheless.

Elvis' sanctuary was chosen wisely. Danger approaching from above would send him bounding down the hill to safety; a hunter below could be avoided by darting a few yards up and over the top of the ridge. He was only three hundred yards from camp, along the crest of the same hill, and he had undoubtedly listened to our laughter around the campfire in the evenings. He was within earshot of our comings and goings, and could easily keep abreast of our whereabouts. Such coolness and strategy were impressive, really impressive.

He was entering his haven from the north end of the ridge, where the slope was easier to negotiate. Next fall, when the wind was right — out of the north at his back — I could sneak into his bedding area well before daylight and ambush him when he returned. I would have to enter camp quietly, without using the jeep, so he wouldn't know I was here. The wind would have to be perfect, too, before I made my move, for I would likely get only one more chance at him.

The track at my feet was the key to his Hideout, and he didn't know I held it.

FIFTEEN

ROM three hundred yards away the big 10 X 56 field glasses brought Elvis' hill into crisp focus. Fractured limestone ledges peeked between trees growing on the hillside. Impenetrable cedars clung to the steepest section near the top, their roots jamming into cracks in the stone. A few of the oaks farther down were already beginning their remarkable transformation to scarlet and orange, though the October afternoon air lay warm on the land. The nights had assumed a lively edge, however, so sitting around a fire in the evenings had become a pleasant necessity.

My family was here for the first hunt of the season, though today I was armed only with binoculars. Until a norther blew through I could merely scout Elvis' sanctuary from a distance, but once the rut started in a few weeks his routine would be shattered and he could appear anywhere. Patience, I kept reminding myself.

With only archery season in progress the deer remained undisturbed. Though alert as always, they moved freely in the mornings and evenings, and we had each seen anywhere from five to a dozen deer every time we sat on stands. Generous rains had fallen during the spring and continued through the summer, and the oaks were all drooping with acorns. The deer weren't yet flocking to the wheat and oat fields as was normal for this time of year. As a result, the boys had been choosing stands in the oak uplands on the front half of the place. Apparently they had chosen wisely, for late yesterday afternoon Reed missed a nice eight point buck, and Lee fired an arrow just over a turkey gobbler.

Around the fire last night they both still bubbled with adrenaline, regaling their mother and me with tales of their missed shots, which grew more extravagant with each retelling. Well I remembered my first hunts when I was their age — the excitement which held sleep at bay for hours the preceding night, before daylight the campfire and the first sip of strong coffee laced with cream, a baptism of cedar smoke, and finally the rising sun revealing a strange, infinitely fascinating landscape of trees and rocks and unknowable flowing creeks. And deer, always the deer, moving like restless spirits in the leaden dawn, does stomping a foot in alarm when they discovered you, and once, mysterious and serene, a buck with spreading, heavy antlers which gave me my first case of the adrenaline shakes, a progressive malady with no known cure in this lifetime. Later, after the day's hunt, we would retire to camp and the disorderly cooking of my father and the other men, sausage and scrambled eggs and green chilis and globs of tangy cheese all mixed together in the big cast-iron skillet, or cans of stew and beans and corn placed in the edge of the fire, or beef ribs sizzling over pulsing mesquite coals.

Lee and Reed had to endure no such rough fare now, however, like I normally prepared, not with their mother along. Our lot was to feast upon roasted quail wrapped in bacon and stuffed with a jalapeño pepper, grilled pork chops from the wild hog marinated in cherry brandy, potatoes Romanoff, green bean casserole, fry bread, and Dutch oven-baked peach cobbler. After such a meal each of us menfolk, young and old, gladly volunteered to wash dishes, though I feared if I stood up too soon my belly might drag the ground like an African lion leaving a kill...

The bugle-clear trilling of passing sandhill cranes drew my

142

attention from Elvis' hillside. I finally located them with the binoculars, very high and far off near the horizon, their long V pointing the way for the colder season to follow. The crane's migration made autumn official, not by the calendar but by the feel, a much more proper way to determine such things. In fact, if the cranes and geese ever become so weak as species that they fail to make their treks, spring and fall might cease to exist, indeed, the earth might well stop spinning on its axis.

My eyes returned to Elvis' alleged abode and immediately focused on a gray log with an upright branch. It looked precisely like a deer, and I probably had peered at it two dozen times already this afternoon. Such things stand out, especially when you're searching for bedded deer, the most difficult ones to find. You look for only pieces of a deer: the straight line of the back, lighter hair on the underside, the twitch of a tail, the angle of the upright ears, but they usually transform into a clump of grass, an odd shadow, a flitting bird, an old log, all of which change like a slow-motion kaleidoscope as the sun progresses. Ten such phantoms might catch your gaze for every deer spotted.

I hadn't actually seen Elvis for almost a year, since missing him from the Skyscraper, nor any sign of him since the single track on the back side of his hill last spring. I'd been careful to give his presumed hideout a wide berth, but today's scouting was in hopes of a distant glimpse of him to confirm my conjecture about his location.

By now, I suppose the questions might fairly be asked, Why bother Elvis at all? Why not just observe rather than try to kill a deer? Reasonable questions, questions I've often pondered during quiet afternoons on a stand. In the absence of four-legged predators — a separate issue already addressed — either eventual starvation or regulated annual hunting will keep the deer population in check. We hunt, in part, to crop the surplus animals and hold the herd within the carrying capacity of the land. Too many deer are just as destructive as too many goats.

In our area, game biologists recommend taking up to twenty percent of the herd each year, roughly the same percentage that pre-Colombian Indians are estimated to have harvested. Here at the Hideout, we now have somewhere around seventy deer, which means we can crop as many as fourteen with no detriment to the herd. Elm and oak and hackberry root-sprouts are being heavily browsed, a sure sign that deer numbers are near capacity: we should probably kill at least eight or ten to keep their total down.

But that is only part of the reason a hunter takes to the woods. Most come primarily for the umbilical connection to place and friends and campfire which can only be consecrated by the focused seeking of an animal on his own terms. The bond vanishes if one just observes and never interacts with the natural world, then retires to camp to dine on food grown and processed a thousand miles away.

And there's this, too. If one eats meat one should be willing, at least occasionally, to kill it oneself, for the hunter experiences first-hand the stalking and waiting and shooting and butchering necessary to place food on the table, and perhaps more importantly, takes direct responsibility for those actions. In fact, one wouldn't have to perform many cerebral gymnastics to maintain that hunting is the morally high road for those who eat meat, that buying commercially raised and processed beef or pork or chicken causes far more distress for the same amount of calories.

It would seem the question of hunting winnows down to three possibilities. Hunting is always wrong, under any circumstance, whether by an ancient hunter/gatherer, a horseback Comanche chasing buffalo, or a modern bowhunter thinning an overpopulated deer herd. Few reasonable people would espouse this view. Or, hunting is always right, under any circumstance, whether a man kills two hundred buffalo a day, hunts whooping cranes, or shoots every deer he sees. No one in his right mind could advocate this interpretation. The third possibility, toward which we have slowly gravitated today, is that hunting is acceptable within thoughtfully erected legal guidelines such as closed seasons, bag limits, and total numbers of permits issued.

It's also time we recognize that to make a place economically viable, the addition of hunting is less disruptive and more supportive of diversified wildlife than ranching alone. Last summer, I saw a golden-cheeked warbler here, an endangered bird which relies upon mature cedar trees and thick brush to nest. Certainly a place like this with hunting as one of its primary focuses requires less livestock and brush clearing to make sense economically, supporting not only more deer but other species, as well, including the endangered ones. Prime hunting land in Texas leases for about five to ten dollars per acre per year, with some ranches offering guided hunts which cost considerably more. If so inclined, I could earn a substantial income from the hunting alone; a lease would pay around five thousand a year and guided bow hunts twice that.

Without question, deer, elk, buffalo, antelope, and turkeys will fare far better if private landowners profit from their presence, and hundreds of other creatures will benefit from the improved habitat, as well. Many landowners who make a portion of their living from hunting are, in fact, hard-core conservationists, with more restrictions on game limits than the state and no sense of humor whatever toward violators. Wildlife is becoming more and more profitable, a positive development which encourages private stewardship of game, a critical factor in the coming years as our public lands face increased use of every kind.

Though animosity has flourished as radicals from both groups have snatched the collective microphone, hunters and wildlife preservation organizations should band together against the authentic enemy of wildlife and wild places, population growth and habitat destruction. But such a union seems sadly unlikely. Hunters won't acknowledge that some of their activities are outrageous, such as the spectacle of Alaskans trapping and snaring wolves so there will be more caribou and moose to hunt, any more than preservationists dare admit that hunter's efforts and money have bolstered wildlife and that carefully controlled sport hunting poses no threat to the species involved. The bickering continues...

As the sun kissed the edge of Elvis' hill, a young coyote appeared on the brushy flat down by the creek. He leaped into the air and pounced with his front feet like a cat, then ate whatever he had caught with an exaggerated smacking. After he repeated the performance a few more times I realized he was catching and eating grasshoppers. A few feet from the coyote's last catch, an armadillo rooted under the leaves for small insects. This should be good, I thought, for any coyote reduced to eating grasshoppers would leap on an armadillo, hard-shell armor and all. The armadillo noticed the coyote first, and incredibly, ran directly toward then under him, causing the startled coyote to leap straight up and take a left. Persisting, the armadillo repeatedly ran after the coyote, who finally trotted away, disgruntled and still looking for a meal. Apparently satisfied with his labors, the armadillo glared for a moment, then returned to the task of making a living in the leaves.

It was fortunate I was sitting here today, or else the excitement of passing sandhill cranes and perverse armadillos would have been missed. Someone has to keep up with these things.

I hoped the boys were having as much entertainment in their stands this evening. Reed had chosen a place we referred to as The Cedar Stand, and Lee waited where a steep hill pinched down close to the creek know as The Funnel. We effortlessly gave names to such places — The Skyscraper Stand, Frank's Brush Blind, Turkey Flats, Whirlpool Falls, for convenience at first but perhaps egotistically thinking that by the naming we possessed them, all the while only vaguely aware that the places were creeping into our souls until ultimately they possessed us instead. They become part of us and we part of them, as the Comanches and others found to their sorrow.

Years ago — decades ago, actually — when I was first married, my new wife and I used to camp at an out of the way place in a National Recreation Area in the Texas panhandle. In the depths of winter we would sleep outside, down sleeping bags zipped together, watching the stars and listening to the horned owls in the grove of ancient cottonwoods around us. Those trees, some of which three people couldn't reach around, watched over us at frosty winter dawn, rustled their leaves with the storms of spring, and offered shade in the indolent heat of summer. For a couple of years we were seldom disturbed on our weekends there and considered the grove of trees in the desolate canyon our own. Then came jobs with their attendant moves, babies, and responsibilities, along with the necessary narrowing of life's focus. Ten years passed before I returned to the far away cottonwood grove. I discovered that the National Park Service, Department of the Interior, United States Government, had bulldozed the trees into an obscene heap, leafless branches reaching helplessly for the sky. In place of the huge cottonwoods stood dozens of thumb-sized Russian Olive trees, an exotic import, staked upright in neat rows. After staring in disbelief, I drove away, never to return.

Yes, becoming too attached to a particular place sooner or later causes emotional seizures. Better to keep one's distance. Don't ever begin thinking of a place as yours or start bestowing names...

Few are fortunate enough to see into the future, but where the Hideout is concerned I've seen ahead clearly. Last summer I visited the nearby ranch of a friend and saw what this place would become. Sumacs and hackberries and white honeysuckle, prime deer foods, grew luxuriously. For the abundant turkeys and other birds were blackberries and dogwood fruit in profusion. Thick native grass held topsoil on the hillsides, where it belonged. Deer wandered everywhere among the thickets and brush, heavy-bodied, mature bucks sporting velveted antlers and sleek does with twin spotted fawns. And so would be this place eventually, if not in my lifetime then certainly in the boys'...

Shadows had crept along the ground and up the trees until they converged and covered everything without a sound, though I listened closely. Blue herons in ones and twos rowed across the sky toward their roost, which had remained in the same place from the oldest memory of my neighbors. The birds settled out of sight on the next ranch downstream, where they squawked and fussed like a crowd of agitated drunks in their big sycamores along the creek. As the light diminished the barbarous noise slowly quieted and they settled for the night.

Just before dark, the big binoculars allowed me to find a doe feeding on the hillside, barely visible except when she took a step. Another doe appeared, moving slowly like the first. In the last gasp of light it appeared they both kept looking behind, back where they had no doubt spent the day bedded down. The illumination had faded, but their actions as much as announced there were other deer with them. I just hoped one of them was Elvis, while considering that the thick cedars near the top of the ridge would offer concealment for a close downhill shot.

Little Sister had now become an extension of my arm. I had continued practicing all summer and was lethal inside of twenty yards, the arrows magically appearing in the chosen spot.

Elvis better not give me another chance.

SIXTEEN

THE rocks and grass between the trees gleamed faintly in the starlight, while the luminous sky hung behind the black velvet lace of the branches overhead. Sharp shadows all around absorbed the light like the yawning mouth of a cave, leaving only a dark void. The sun still had given no hint of its future plans. A stream of frosty air, like God's breath, flowed softly from the left, out of the north. With moccassined feet, I quietly shifted position in the darkness and waited, balanced on a boulder nestled between two bushes.

Earlier, I stirred the coals of last night's fire and placed green cedar branches on them, then washed *Little Sister* in the smoke. But I reflected that my chances may have already expired. I had been pursuing Elvis for two years now. Or was it three? With the coming of this cold front, well before daylight I had sneaked into what I hoped was his daytime sanctuary and waited for him to return from his nightly rambling.

This was my last card to play unless Elvis offered another accidental shot during the coming rut. I didn't think he would. He might well be unhuntable, the current effort at getting inside his head fruitless. An animal's senses and motivations are so different from ours that understanding their consciousness is like describing colors to a blind man. We inhabit the same earth, but their world is far different. Deer see well at night, much better than us, but for all we know may also have infrared vision. With our feeble sense of smell we are only vaguely aware of the role it plays in a deer's life, and they may have other senses with no human correlation, at which we can only guess. To allow their incredible migrations twice each year, sandhill cranes and geese must have some innate ability to follow terrain, an inner mapping system impossible for us to understand. Butterflies see ultraviolet light which we can't perceive; ants somehow communicate with complex chemicals; snakes use their tongues to find prey. All animals live, it seems, within spheres of consciousness defined by their senses. Only partially does a portion of our circle overlap theirs, giving us common ground where we can interpret and imperfectly understand their view of the world. I suppose man is the only animal who uses his mind to travel outside the sphere of his senses. Which doesn't mean that man is the only animal who reasons, though some experts insist humans stand unique in this respect...

Wearing no camo clothing, just wool in muted colors, I wanted nothing artificial, no treestand, no synthetics, nothing to interfere with the natural connection to this place today. The mental machinery quieted and my breathing slowed until I experienced the sensation of disappearing into the earth, merging with the rocks and dirt, becoming invisible not only physically but mentally. With the upper brain shut down, the lower brain functioned as an antenna, until finally I wore these woods like an overcoat.

The sun must have been making a half-hearted attempt at rising, for a whispy light had begun chasing the darkness toward the west. One quail whistled, then after a moment another and another, until five or ten or twenty took up the song to the furthest reaches of my hearing. Other birds joined in the brief burst of noise until, as if a flare had been fired as a signal, they stopped in unison and silence flooded back.

Time passed. A minute, perhaps, or maybe twenty.

My senses vibrated with information — the rustle of a leaf as a sigh of air moved through the branches, the quiet presence of nearby trees, the chill of the air seeping through my clothing, the solid, rough surface of the rock through the thin leather moccasins. I felt rather than heard a sound somewhere in my subconscious. A deer was coming, silent as the sunrise; I could feel its steps through the soles of my feet. After a few moments a doe appeared down the hill fifteen yards. Behind her came another, a yearling. Then another doe. They all stopped, looking behind them. The frost gleamed on their backs, their winter coats fluffed out until they looked as round as barrels. Steam surged from their nostrils as they sifted the air for danger. I could hear them breathing.

The single doe nibbled at a sprout at the base of an oak. Another deer moved behind the cedars, this one bigger than the others. It stopped. A minute passed, then two. Deer hold fifth degree black belts in waiting. Minutes crept by. The other deer continued moving about, but this one remained motionless, watching and listening. Though I had yet to see an antler, with primordial intuition I somehow knew it was Elvis. He still didn't move, and it occurred to me that with his caution he might very well be searching for me.

I suppose some might view modern hunting as evolution in reverse, taking only the biggest and best instead of the weak and slow. Actually, those who hunt exclusively for trophy deer fail to kill very many. In this part of Texas, helicopter surveys estimate that ten percent of the bucks are mature like Elvis, four and a half years of age or older. But despite hunter's best efforts, only a fraction of one percent of the deer killed each year are bucks of this age group, a fact which illustrates that most male deer who reach maturity finally die of starvation when their teeth wear out or coyotes catch them when they're left exhausted after the rut.

Though it sounds ridiculous at first blush, the way to have more such big bucks is to kill only big bucks. Almost every deer herd contains the genetics for large antlers, and if deer numbers are kept within the land's capacity to support them they should receive plenty of nutrition. The third key to antler growth is the age of the deer. Only a buck who has attained full body size at four and a half years can use his energy for building large antlers.

He will reach his peak for two or three years thereafter before beginning a decline in both body condition and rack. Few hunters ever see such a wise deer, settling instead for any buck they can find, cutting short one more adolescent buck's potential. The percentages say that there should be another mature buck at the Hideout besides Elvis, but I've never caught a glimpse of him and or seen a clue to his presence, which helps explain why so many younger bucks are shot by hunters out of desperation. But if more would hold out for a deer like Elvis, the demographics of the herd would change and instead of only a couple of large bucks on a place this size, after a few years there would be half a dozen. Although, after reflection, that many deer the size of Elvis might permanently fry a bowhunter's circuits...

Balancing on three legs, the yearling used a hind foot to scratch behind her neck. One of the does cocked her ears at the hidden deer. It took a couple of steps and I finally saw through the veil of branches that it was, indeed, The King. His antlers were huge, and it was hard to believe that a deer of such size lived right here under my nose. Heavy and dark with ten points, the movement of his rack seemed amplified by his every motion. With a start, I noticed that he had grown slightly pot-bellied with age and had a few gray hairs showing around his face, very much like the predator watching from twenty yards away.

After sniffing the ground Elvis glanced about, then moved again, headed for a clearing in the trees. I remained one with the rocks, scarcely breathing. *Little Sister* seemed to draw the arrow herself as he stepped into the open below me with the other deer. From long practice, my eyes locked on a spot on the shoulder. I didn't consciously release, but abruptly watched the arrow bury to the feathers precisely where my eyes had focused.

The doe lurched down the hill thirty yards, bounced off of a tree, then tumbled and slid into the leaves. She thrashed about trying to rise, but grew weak as the darkness eventually waiting for us all embraced her. She kicked a couple of times and was finally still.

The other deer all jumped when the doe crashed down the hill, but were unsure what happened, unsure of the danger. They looked at the doe, then nervously at each other.

Elvis took a step and stopped, one front foot raised. He tossed his head back, muzzle elevated. Steam puffed from his nose in short bursts as he drank in the air.

"I had you that time," I croaked.

Elvis spun, staring toward me in disbelief, nostrils flared. He stood frozen for an instant, then turned and melted into the brush without a sound. The other doe and yearling vanished, though I never knew where.

Suddenly, my legs shook and I bent, hands on knees, mouth open like a beached carp trying to get the first real breath in an hour, it seemed. My hands and arms tingled as though a charge of electricity flowed through them.

It occured to me that the doe laying down the hill was the essence of the Hideout. For the forbs and acorns and flowing springs here were all within her, just as were winter's winds and summer's warmth. Oats from the field and the musty earth and limestone rocks from the bed of an ancient sea had formed her blood and bones and flesh. Eating her meat would be partaking of a portion of the Hideout, and she would become part of me as had this place, long ago.

Having almost quit shaking, I began side-stepping stiffly down the slope. She lay in the leaves, relaxed and perfect of form. The arrow snapped off when she tumbled and the only sign of her fate was a splotch of blood on her ribs. I knelt, laying a hand on the thick hair of her side and deep within its softness felt her warmth.

After a moment, I reached back into the quiver to find the bundle of dried sage Jim Welch had given me, then placed it beside the deer's mouth. I fumbled open a waterproof container and scraped a match across a nearby rock to ignite it. The hissing match caused the sage to flare for a moment before smoldering, the clean fragrance drifting on the breeze.

You get what you come for every time you venture into the woods on a hunt.

Sometimes, sometimes, you even make a kill.

The Traditional Bowyer's Bibles

Available From Bois d'Arc Press

Bows and Arrows of the Native Americans -Jim Hamm	$14.95
The Traditional Bowyer's Bible, Vol. 1	$19.95
The Traditional Bowyer's Bible, Vol. 2	$22.95
The Traditional Bowyer's Bible, Vol. 3	$24.95
Longbow: A Social and Military History - Robert Hardy	$24.95
Ishi and Elvis - Jim Hamm	$19.95

Please include $3.50 shipping and handling per order.

Bois d'Arc Press
PO Box 233
Azle, TX 76098